THE UNIFIED SYSTEM
CONCEPT OF NATURE

COLLEGE EDITION

by

STEPHEN TH. BORNEMISZA, Ph.D.

Vantage Press, Inc., New York

To the unfading memory of
that Nestor of modern physics
my revered teacher

MAX PLANCK

I dedicate this book
in gratitude

CONTENTS

PREFACE

If you have had your attention directed to the novelties in thought in your own lifetime, you will have observed that almost all really new ideas have a certain aspect of foolishness when they are first produced, and almost any idea which jogs you out of your current abstractions may be better than nothing.—A. N. WHITEHEAD.

Although many branches of science show many similarities, and identical or isomorphic laws have been disclosed in completely different fields of learning, there are many formidable barriers like those between physics and biology, as well as between their various sub-divisions. Whether "life" is to be explained in terms of known "physical principles" or whether "transcendent elements" must be added is one of the problems that still puzzle scientists today.

The present volume contains no mathematics nor formulas to speak of; the main objective is a new approach to conceiving and understanding the unification of physical and biological conceptions including psychology arrived at by the inductive mode of thinking: *asking nature the right question in the right way.* The answer is the unified system concept, evolved by the author in twenty years of study, possibly giving room simultaneously for the idea of Einstein's continuous universe and for the singularities of the quantum theory.

It is not because he has solved the riddle of the universe that man has ceased to wonder about seemingly obvious events in nature, it is rather because he has accustomed himself to the laws of his own personal environment and to taking too many things for granted. The greater our understanding of nature, the more we realize the importance of basic knowledge and the handicaps of overdone technological specialization, even though specialization is an inevitable feature of progress. Only the still incomplete understanding of the very foundations of nature is responsible for the fact that mathematical logic does not succeed in overcoming the intellectual schism involving causality on one hand and randomness on the other.

In the first part of this little book the unified system concept will be discussed in a more general way covering all the individual systems of the universe and their assemblage. The second part deals with the more special systems of organic life, and the Appendix finally will attempt the integration of the realms of experiences and sensations into the physical system concept by suitable psychophysical co-ordination.

STEPHEN THYSSEN BORNEMISZA, PH.D.

Havana, Cuba, April, 1955

PART ONE

THE TWO BASIC PROCESSES OF ALL NATURE

Chapter I

THE RECURRENT AND THE STRUCTURAL CHANGES

I. *Causality and Randomness.*

Science no longer ascribes randomness or chance in nature to mere human ignorance of the natural order. Random elements are real and plain facts, and they are connected with many physical phenomena, although in varying degree. The absence of random elements in nature would imply a purely mechanical universe in which everything is completely determined and linked up by a continuous chain of cause and effect. This particular kind of togetherness is known by such terms as "causality," "the law of causation," "determinateness," and "mechanism." Complete orderliness in nature could be possible only if continuity, reversibility, permanence of action, eternal recurrence, stability, and equilibrium were omnipresent.

In our everyday lives we constantly meet with a peculiar mixture of cause and chance. Take the activities within a subway station, for instance. Nearly every person entering the station knows where to go and how to proceed. But in spite of each person's predetermined pattern of behavior to catch his train, he is forced to make unforeseen detours and unpredictable movements in order to avoid other people bent on a like goal. The entire process represents the constant intersection of causality by random elements.*

---

* In this present treatise the terms "randomness," "chance," "indeterminateness," are used in a more general meaning, in the sense of "not to be known beforehand," and should not be associated with Heisenberg's principle of indeterminacy.

Another familiar example is the relation between the striking of a match and the heat produced by the flame after the match has been set alight. Undoubtedly there is a causal connection between these two effects, but there is no continuous chain of cause and effect that leads from the striking of the match to the random movements of the agitated air molecules surrounding the flame, which account for the sensation of heat. The agitated molecules do not behave in an orderly or predetermined way; they are irregular, chaotic, irreversible, conflicting, statistical, or any other term we prefer to describe their indeterminateness. Again we have to conclude that in spite of a valid causal law in respect to generality, no individual movement is uniquely determined.

The exposition so far could suggest the idea that chance is a strange, even malignant, force that deflects the orderly progression of occurrences from the more perfect path. On the contrary, chance provides more abundant opportunities for lawful progression by making it impossible to escape one set of laws without entering the field of another. As a switchboard mechanism shifts calls from one line to another, so chance shifts events.

Why nature makes use of a kind of switchboard system is of great significance, however. The switchboard mechanism, because of its flexibility and plasticity, can adjust to emergencies. And emergencies are bound to happen continually within a complex system like our universe. It is rather difficult to imagine how a rigid and purely mechanical universe can be prevented from falling to pieces unless there is a way of correcting mistakes and disturbances by switching away from chains of cause and effect leading perhaps to unavoidable disaster. Thus nature employs indeterminateness, randomness, chance, or probability to keep things running smoothly.

There is nothing very novel or interesting to be immediately deduced from the ideas just mentioned. We shall try, however, to separate the cause elements and the chance elements of nature in order to study their interrelation and their relative importance. By this procedure we shall gain a new and basic understanding of the general patterns according to which our universe is likely to operate. The splitting up of all infinitesimal changes in nature and a renewed appropriate composition of them enable us to arrive at processes which belong to one of two fundamentally different groups represented by causality and by indeterminateness only. Already in our normal daily life we meet with a conservative principle of repetition or recurrence in addition to the unpredictable event, and it is the former upon which is based our conviction of the lawfulness of nature.

The events of the first group are generally distinguished by the fact that they can be represented by constant effective values. Such is always the case whenever an event consists of separate restorable and consecutive cyclic processes, the sequence of cycles being isochronal. The respective condition of the systems and objects involved is characterized by the phase, and, obeying a certain rule, is recurrently restored after the lapse of a certain period of time. We shall term such periodic or circular transformations, which occur over and over again, *"recurrent changes."* These effects of this kind of circular causation involve only temporary alteration of the organization of a definite system, its basic character remaining intact. In the extreme case, these processes are stationary in any period and do not change the nature of the system at all. Such a round of change occurs ideally in any purely mechanical system, as in a flywheel rotating forever in a vacuum on frictionless bearings.* All things in existence have some degree of permanence and persistence; they remain the same and retain their identity amid the general flux of events for a long time.

The second group of events comprises all those which interrupt the uniformity and the rigid causality of a purely mechanical universe by continually transforming the structure of an actual system, which is the analogue of friction

---

* Ideal recurrent changes representing repetition in every respect are non-realizable in any concrete case. The term "recurrent changes" used by the author includes nonideal periodic wave forms. The mathematical treatment of this kind of wave forms is discussed in a book of E. Weber, *Linear Analysis*, Vol. I, New York, 1954.

in a rotating flywheel. After the concurrence of such uni-directional or nonrecurrent "*structural changes*," which usually happen unsystematically and once only, a previous phase of the system cannot be regained in the former manner, despite unchanging external conditions.

The structural changes include the structuralization and disintegration of atoms; the reduction of mass of stars by radiation; the growth and death of organisms; radioactive decay; the retardation of the earth's revolution by the tides; the wear and tear on a machine; the erection of a building or its collapse; the manufacture or destruction of commodi-ties: in short, any alteration of nature in which the structure is changed without the initial situation of the system con-cerned being restored.

It is the merit of biology to have recognized the characteristic difference between these two basic groups, from the illimitable number of events of which we have quoted a few examples. Biology knows of functional processes as opposed to structural and pathological changes; of dynamic stability as opposed to slow decay. Medicine discusses the cyclic processes of maintaining normal performance, termed homeostasis, as opposed to the wasting, strangling forces by which men die. Even in history, patterns of recurrence and of uniqueness are distinguished by historians like Toynbee.

In spite of the differing terminology, it seems evident that in each case we have to deal with the same contradistinction. Accordingly, we would distinguish between "*life*" and "*evolu-tion*," understanding by "life" the metabolic power, includ-ing pulsation, respiration, the alternation of waking and sleeping, working and resting, sexual periodicity, assimila-tion, etc., and by "evolution," birth, growth, ageing, death, propagation, wear, regeneration, and so on. Both the de-pendability of recurrent changes and the novelty or spon-taneity of structural changes are everywhere.

The observation of the two groups of natural processes mentioned above constitutes the foundations of quite a new viewpoint in the contemplation and investigation of nature. We have to emphasize that the characteristics rendering possible their distinction are of a purely physical reality, as will be explained in the course of Part One.

In the following pages we shall be less concerned with changes affecting the microscopic elements of nature—individual atoms, electrons, quanta, etc.—since they afford of special treatment. We will concern ourself mainly with the so-called macroscopic domain, or still more clearly expressed, we will deal mostly with processes where the laws of thermodynamics may be applied without hesitation. Sometimes, however, we shall refer to individual atoms and molecules for reason of generalization.

2. *The Recurrent Changes*

It has already been stated that the recurrent changes consist of partial processes of a cyclic rhythm, and that the separate cycles are isochronal. They consist in a succession of individual processes, each of which is termed a cycle, cyclic progress, circulation, rotation, revolution, circle, round, tour, turn, course, oscillation, wave, etc. At the end of such a cyclic process, the initial situation or phase of the respective system is restored; neither heat nor work, neither latent nor free energy have been either gained or lost at any point of the reference system or by it.

Any differential transformation of the system during a cyclic process is canceled by some other, so that, striking a balance in relation to a suitably selected time interval, they eliminate each other. The basic elements may, indeed, have been replaced so that the identity of the system concerned in its final and its initial phase relates to its organization only and not to its substance. The structure of the system alone remains constant or unchangeable, whereas the separate elemental particles may be exchanged for others of a similar kind.

An example of a process without any consequences for a system is the cycle of activation or ionization of an atom or a molecule and its return to a low-energy condition. Whether such activation or ionization is effected by atomic, molecular, ionic, or electronic impulses, by photoelectrical processes, as the Compton process, or in any other way, and whether the atoms or molecules on their return into their original state are radiating X rays or waves of a lesser frequency, and whether the dissipated energy is emitted in the form of radiation, thermokinematically, or in any other way, is of no importance whatsoever for the systems concerned. Nor does it make any difference at all whether the nature of the phenomenon is described as luminescence, thermal luminosity, fluorescence, sensitized fluorescence, resonance effect, Raman effect, or by any other term. The atom or molecule returns to its initial condition after any number of cyclic processes without having suffered a recognizable structural change.

Futher examples of such cyclic processes are the dispersion of light through the medium of molecules or dust particles (Tyndall effect), the "heating" of molecules by the absorption of light, and the subsequent emission of kinematic or wave energy by radiation of electromagnetic waves; the so-called airglow; the heat convection of the molecules by thermokinematic accumulation from the surrounding medium and by thermokinematic emission to the environment; the cyclic nucleal oscillation of molecules; the circulation of electrons within atomic and molecular groups; the rotational motion of waves on the nuclear surface; the spin of electrons and positrons; the cyclic changes of celestial bodies, the orbits of the stars, particularly the revolution of the earth causing summer and winter, day and night, freezing and thawing; the revolution of the moon provoking the tides; the circulation of water on the earth's surface including evaporation, cloud formation and motion, condensation, formation of ice, dew, rain, snowfalls and hailstorms, water currents, formation of lakes and seas, and so on; the thermal circulation of the earth, including winds, atmospheric currents, volcanic action, and so on; the metabolism of the earth with its quantitative excretion of chemical matter and fusion of dissimilar substances, and so on.

Innumerable cyclic processes of this kind are observable in plants, animals, and their communities in organic nature. A peculiar feature of all organisms is metabolism, which, in many animals, is connected with the circulation of the blood and the pulsation of the heart, with respiration, nutrition, and excretion, waking and sleeping, work and rest, with the circulation of heat produced by internal combustion and, by conduction, transferred to the environment.

Plants as well as animals exhibit a great number of vital phenomena of a rhythmic nature. Some instances are the hibernal torpor of the trees; the periodic opening and closing of many blossoms; nyctitropism of certain plants; the periodic discharge of the germinative cells of certain algae; the periodicity of growth and nucleal division.

Complete cycles occurring in a larger community are the circulation of money within an economic system; the output and change of shifts at a factory; the turnover of a business concern; the course or term of an educational institution; the work of public institutions or a library; transportation by public transport systems; the vital manifestations of a town; a change of employees at an office; the traffic in a street; the arrival and departure of guests at a hotel; the visitors to a museum; the customers of a department store, and so on. Cyclic processes in the lives of generations of animal and plant species may be the transformations of the individual specimens, their metamorphoses and alternations of generations, their birth and death, flowering and fading, growth and decay.

We notice cyclic processes even with artificial creations produced by man, to mention only the running of machines, automatons, and clocks. Cyclic processes are the swinging motion of a pendulum; the charging and discharging of a condenser in an oscillating electromagnetic circuit; dilation and contraction by the alternating pressure of a solid but elastic body; the compression and expansion of a gas under constant pressure by alternately cooling or heating it; the magnetization and demagnetization of metal bodies; the formation of chemical compounds and their decomposition into their former components, and so forth. The burning of a flame, the play of a fountain, and the like are almost stationary processes.

The examples enumerated so far mostly represent independently working or self-maintaining systems, or processes in which the system itself takes some active part. There are, however, objects which suffer complete cycles being forced upon the majority of their parts from without, or whose cyclic processes are at least activated or released from without. We term such objects "commodities." They comprise clothes, household goods, tools, instruments, storage batteries, books, music scores, parks, places of worship, currency, documents, buildings, dwellings, caves, webs, snail shells, beehives, birds' nests, coral, and so on. Although the cyclic processes resulting from the use of these objects are suffered passively, it is nevertheless a fact that they also return to their initial condition after each employment. They obey the same mysterious laws controlling the continuity of life, although even the miraculous powers issuing the orders and watching over the fulfillment are, in this case, to be found outside the systems in question.

Every event within a cyclic process represents a "phasic change." Whether a certain event is a phasic change or not is commonly recognizable only if the complete cyclic process is known. We mean here cyclic processes within a limited space and not reversible processes in a thermodynamic sense, for the fictitious boundary constitutes no actual barrier; it can be transgressed by matter; it is actually nothing but a characterization of a definite space-time section.

In nature, the structure of any individual system is adapted to its surrounding medium, being, on the whole, stable and subject solely to systematic alterations, so that cyclic processes of natural and artificial structures actually recur with a certain regularity, provided that a suitable time interval is chosen for observation. They are temporally isochronal, therefore we are justified in speaking of cyclic processes of definite systems. This is a well-known fact with regard to living organisms, where the separate successive cyclic processes are multiformly interlaced, so that the initiation of a new cyclic process is not subject to chance.

Nature can nowhere be switched off like a machine, for it incessantly performs its monotonous and uniform work. So, recurrent changes are phenomena to be met with everywhere in nature, science, technics, sociology, and culture. The fact that there is an essential difference between the recurrent changes of organic and inorganic natures, between the recurrent changes of the organisms and their technical creations, is well known to us, yet of no importance here where our task is only to disclose the features common to all spheres. Although examples of recurrent changes may be found in all branches of the natural sciences, we must not forget that we are concerned with a physically defined phenomenon. Our examples in no way constitute mere similarities, but are energetical realities.

The recurrent changes are, in an energetic respect, always of the same type as the functioning of a self-acting and ideal machine, i.e. a machine not subject to wear and tear, whose performed work is stationary in the mean and whose intensity of work is constant in an ever-regenerating environment. Such a machine, under normal external conditions — starting and stopping, charging, accumulating and expending energy — is continually returning to its initial phase or its original condition. The cycles of such a self-acting machine working together with its surrounding medium will always be completed by a return to the starting point, and at every return to its initial situation the organization of the machine will also revert to its original situation, including its energy and entropy.* *The transformations of energy effected by the recurrent changes of the machine appear solely in the en-*

---

* "Like energy, entropy is in the first instance a measure of something that happens when one state is transformed into another. Thermodynamics shows that for reversible (recoverable) processes the integral is independent of the intermediate details and depends only on the initial and final states. *It is the recoverability of the original situation that is important, not the detailed reversal of the steps which led to the original departure from the initial situation.* When entropy-increasing processes take place in a system, its capacity to deliver mechanical work decreases, and the amount of entropy increase is proportional to the loss of capacity to deliver work. This may be expressed by saying that the increase of entropy is a measure of 'degradation' of energy or of the loss of 'availability' of the energy of the system." P. W. Bridgman. *The Nature of Thermodynamics*, Harvard University Press, 1943.

*vironment, quantitatively and qualitatively constant in the
average.* Our view is in no way affected by whether this
mechanism is simple or complicated, known or unknown, so
that we need not restrict it to a limited group of systems.
All the systems ranging from atoms to communities of
organisms are vehicles of recurrent changes.

Recurrent changes do not include phenomena like injury
and regeneration; wounding, healing; illness, convalescence;
accident, recovery; destruction, reconstruction; wastage, restoration damage, repair; and many others. These phenomena represent, as a rule, irregular, frequent unique, events
caused by abnormal and extraordinary conditions. At any
rate, they are not recurrent cyclic processes, and it is therefore impossible in their case to speak of a constant mean
intensity or of constant effective values at all. It is interesting
to observe that recurrent changes always must be determined
and predictable, if the whole system is considered without
regard to the intermediate stages.

3. *Structural Changes*

Alterations which continually transform the structure,
the organization, or the build of a system manifest themselves by an alteration of the quality of the recurrent changes
and of the quantity of the effective transformative intensity.
They may be distributed discretely and unsystematically, being frequently accompanied by a change in name and nature
of the system in question; or in the nature of processes of
protracted duration they may even continue parallel to the
recurrent changes. Structural changes become manifest as
the transformation, origination, or decay of individuals,
systems, and things. Any structural change is in any case
unique for the system because any further change already
meets with a structure other than that encountered by the
previous one.

Some examples from inorganic nature are decay or disintegration by radioactivity, the cooling of the planets, the
disintegration and explosion of novae, the solidifying of

heavy metals, the weathering of rocks, earthquakes and volcanic eruptions, the ageing of mountains, and many changes of the celestial bodies and their systems. Further examples are the change of phase of a substance in coagulation, freezing, crystallization, melting, evaporation, condensation, sublimation, the change or modification of a substance due to alteration of external conditions, the decomposition of a chemical compound by heating, the creation of new chemical compounds, the combustion or explosion of substances, the formation and fission of atoms and molecules, the natural decomposition of atoms, cloud formation, the dispersal of a cloud with or without precipitation, the electrical discharge of the atmosphere by lightning, denudation of the earth's surface, stratification and rock formation, diagenesis and metamorphosis, lamination, petrifaction, and so on.

Structural changes in organic nature are the florescence and withering of plants, the birth and death of animals, fecundation and pollination, cell division, mutations, the acquisition of individual qualities, accomplishments, experiences, and knowledge, the building of houses, hives, webs, and so on.

Structural changes in communities are the founding of a family, club, organization, business, state, the flourishing of a nation, the growth of a town, the expansion of a commercial enterprise or its decline by reason of mismanagement, the growth of a business by the establishment of branch offices, the intensification or slackening of a friendship or league, the change in a nation's government, a rebellion, a revolution, the canceling of a treaty, evolution, revolts, mutiny, overthrow, the rise of diplomatic complications or other conflicts, the outbreak of wars, the initiation of peace negotiations, the emergent evolution of new biological species, and so forth.

Examples of structural changes may be found also in the technical cultural products of the organisms, such as the wear and tear of machines, the burning away of candles, the stopping of clocks, the corrosion of metal objects, the rotting of wooden articles, the decay of foodstuffs, dilapidation of buildings, the burning out of electric lamps or fuses, the destruction caused by a short circuit, and the like. And to the degree that recuperation, convalescence, restoration, regeneration, repair, and the like do not represent recurrent changes, they also belong to the category of structural changes.

The cause of structural changes is generally traceable to immediate external forces. Transformations effected by external influences are the so-called splitting of atoms; the destruction of crystals or other solid bodies by dissolution or some other external force of pressure and tension, particularly breaking, tearing, grinding, smashing, bending, and so on; the mutual destruction of living beings in the struggle of life; their illness, disablement, or death due to some accident such as stumbling, falling from a height, being buried alive, infection, poisoning, injury, starvation, thirst, suffocation; homicide for motives of personal enmity; the decline of an economic enterprise through competitive rivalry or boycott; the invasion and destruction of a town; the subjugation of a people; the ruination of a family, an association or a state, by external enemies; the retardation of the earth's rotation by the tides; the change of the earth's surface by shrinkage, hydrocirculation and thermal circulation; the disintegration of cosmic fragments in their meteoric fall; the nonelastic deformation of solid bodies; the building of shelters, webs, caves, houses, nests, especially snail shells, birds' nests, spiders' webs, coral reefs, wasps' nests, beehives, termitaria, beavers' lodges, ant hills, and so on; the rise of towns, factories, bridges, canals, places of worship, plantations, and the like; the production of machines, apparatus, instruments, commodities, garments, household goods, tools; the writing of books, the composing of music; the painting of pictures, or any creative work of an artistic, scientific, literary, or technical nature; but also the damaging of objects, the wearing out of machines by employment, the demolition of any structure, the destruction of animate life and civilizations by war and natural catastrophies; and the breeding of new biological species; the keeping of domestic animals; the capture and taming of animals of all kinds;

the rearing of progeny; the exertion of influence upon our fellow-beings by compulsion, by oral or printed word, or their conversion by example, and so forth.

This is but a small selection of processes or events which, as already pointed out, by irregularity or uniqueness of occurrence are not part of the constant properties of a system. It must be noted, however, that not every alteration of a recurrent change necessarily signifies a structural change also; for instance, if these alterations become recurrent changes themselves, i.e. if they occur periodically.

A typical example of this kind is the double pendulum simultaneously performing both short- and long-period oscillations. Although the balance is constantly shifting away from the short-period oscillations, the mean state of balance can remain unaltered, thus actually suffering no structural change at all. Whether the system will regain its initial phase is, as a rule, not recognizable until after the completion of the longest period. In general, to be absolutely certain it is advisable to consider time periods sufficiently protracted to permit of a definite judgment as to whether a process really constitutes a structural change, or whether it is merely a phase of a recurrent change. This becomes quite obvious when the graphical curve of some complicated, periodically recurrent function is examined. A curve section indiscriminately chosen reveals little as to the nature of the completed curve.

Structural changes may derive from either of two possible causes. On the one hand, a structural change may result from an internal reorganization of a system; on the other, an alteration of the surrounding medium may be the primary cause of a secondary structural change in a system. Growth, ageing, and wear and tear are structural changes of the former kind, but most other structural changes will be found to be of the latter nature.

4. *Relations between Recurrent and Structural Changes*

If by classification of all natural processes under the

headings of recurrent changes and structural changes respectively an attempt has been made to draw a sharp line of distinction between determination and chance, we do not by any means contend that in nature we actually encounter their spatial and temporal isolation. In the first place, this classification is intended merely to represent a purely conceptual distinction, just as, for instance, mechanical processes are subdivided into frictionless mechanics, on the one hand, and frictional, on the other; or as an oscillating electromagnetic field is split up into a primary and a secondary portion.

In all probability, the recurrent changes never remain constant, but will always, in one way or other, conduce to a structural change. Technology, at any rate, has not as yet succeeded in constructing a device not liable to wear and tear. Just as friction is inevitably caused by motion, so does any phasic change apparently inevitably involve a structural change. These conditions are perhaps best exemplified by the picture of a spiral motion which may be split up into a rotational and a vector motion. In this case, one rotation resulting in the return of the object to its initial position represents a completed cyclic process, the respective rotational angle the phase of this cyclic process. Structural changes are represented by a vector going through the center, so that finally a spiral curve results.

There is, first of all, a close connection in organic nature wherever life and evolution are never at a standstill, wherever the recurrent changes directly and powerfully influence both the structural changes and the evolutionary processes, and wherever any protracted cessation of vital activity will invariably result in death. Every vital process influences the constitution of the organism and is in quite a definite way linked with simultaneous growth and ageing. A regular and expedient way of life, for instance, will in general insure healthy development, whereas licentiousness will engender ill health and deformation. A normal and unimpeded amplification of life conditions healthy development, while vital functions encumbered by hardships or interference will check progress and cause premature death. A considerable quantitative diminution in food may lead to inanition and stunt all natural faculties. Often enough there is an unmistakable causal connection between a person's diseases and his mode of living. The prosperity of a nation and the development of the natural faculties of a human being are but the issue of their respective lives.

Retardation of the earth's rotation is determined by the rhythm and intensity of the tides; the degree of wastage of commodities and machines, by their employment. The hypothetical shrinking process of the mantle depends on the exchange of radiation on the earth's surface; geological evolution (denudation, stratification, diagenesis, metamorphosis, and so on) is dictated by the intensity of hydrocirculation, including winds, as well as by other recurrent changes of the earth proper. In neither of these cases can evolution be checked.

A clear discrimination between recurrent changes and structural changes seems possible in a wide sphere of nature, like, for instance, in atoms, molecules, and crystals. Atoms and molecules and many crystals are not affected in their nature, as far as can be observed, either by heat convection or by temporary activation and ionization, or by any other cyclic participation in the turnover of energy. If, after a number of cyclic processes, they return to their initial phase, no trace of any permanent structural change can be detected. Though correlation between phasic and structural changes is not known, it may yet be discovered.

Even if, according to the above examples, the classification of all processes into recurrent and structural changes can usually be effected in respect of conception only, such a systematization does not, on the other hand, merely constitute an idle sport or an absolutely arbitrary construction of a purely formal nature. The conceptual separation of the basic processes is by no means comparable to the splitting up of a vector into two fictitious components directed arbitrarily, but only practicable in one way, like, for instance, the division of a complex number into its real and imaginary parts. As pointed out before, both the recurrent and the structural changes possess a physical reality, and are directly deducible from experience and experiment. And even though the two groups of phenomena are closely intertwined, their border line is never indistinct or vague, so that at all events we are struck by the unmistakable contradistinction of the two kinds. In principle, they may be distinguished at any time and in any place, and nature herself has often facilitated a clear discrimination.*

However, one must not conclude that the bipartition of all processes is logically self-evident just because it conforms to nature. Considered from the viewpoint of logic, it is not strange that nature should change according to its whims, and that here or there something novel should occur. *But that an old condition long since passed should, from the infinite abundance of possibilities, be selected anew in order to be reproduced once more is the most astounding fact that nature discloses.* Our experience teaches us that we can nevertheless encounter such processes in nature over and over again. And if that is so, we must take it as a distinct indication of the fact that forces obeying circular causation must be at work here, forces aiming at the preservation of just this particular case and whose character may be discovered solely by experience.

Metaphorically speaking, nature is endowed with a memory, a retentive faculty, which leads over and over again back into the past. The atom excited and ionized ever anew does not tire of striving for the reattainment of the initial state;

---

* No method depending upon Fourier Analysis can strictly be applied to nonlinear problems. Nevertheless, an approximation may be obtained by omitting all harmonics and dealing with relations between the fundamentals of the variations only, as though the harmonics did not exist. If, for instance, a quantity A is dependent on a quantity B in some nonlinear manner, and if B is varied sinusoidally, A will vary, as a result, not sinusoidally but periodically, with the same frequency. The motion of A may, therefore, be harmonically analyzed and the fundamental of the input-frequency may be determined. The phase and relative amplitude of the fundamental are functions of the frequency of the input, and in distinction from a linear system, are functions also of the amplitude of the input. Thus a self-maintaining condition will require a particular amplitude, as well as a particular frequency. (A. Tustin. "A method of analyzing the effect of certain kinds of nonlinearity in closed cycle control systems," J.I.E.E., Vol. 94, Part II, No. 1, 1947).

the darkest night is indeed succeeded by a bright day. Every-thing we do, every thought and action, depends on recall, on the ability to repeat experiences over and over again.

Statistics in general are applicable only if events should happen over and over again, for probability calculus cannot be based on the unique event. Therefore the recurrent changes presuppose statistics in general. If the recurrent changes are composed of isochronal cycles, the calculated probabilities will be very accurate indeed, practically cer-tainties, and the causality concept may be applied without hesitation. On the other hand, if structural changes are affecting the recurrent changes, random elements will be introduced to render invalid the causality concept. The rigid causality of classical physics just seems to be the expression for a limital condition, the reliability of the causality concept, depending on the nature of the structural changes.

5. Relativity of Recurrent and Structural Changes

It is a well-known fact that one and the same functional relationship may be recorded in a graphical diagram in wide-ly divergent ways. The picture finally obtained depends on the frame of reference and the scale. Polar co-ordinates yield a different representation from those at right angles; likewise common scales from logarithmic graphs. Despite the disparity in the methods of representation, none is wrong; they merely vary in their efficacy and lucidity.

With recurrent changes and structural changes, the picture alters if the frame of reference alters. Whether we have to deal with a recurrent change or a structural change depends essentially upon the reference system underlying the speculation. A few examples may here eluci-date this point.

The transformation in the atmosphere of electromagnetic waves of high frequency into similar waves of low frequency signifies for the atoms and molecules in question, and for the atmosphere in particular, nothing but a recurrent change;

for the waves and photons, on the other hand, it represents a structural change. The metabolism of animals constitutes a recurrent change for the organisms themselves; it represents, however, a structural change for the substances consumed and the oxygen inhaled. Budding, florescence, and ripening belong to the recurrent changes of plants, though constituting structural changes for the organs in question. With regard to the human being, his birth, growth, ageing, and death are stages in his development; with respect to mankind they are merely various phases of its vital functions, as the death of one human individual is generally compensated by the birth of another. The main stock or structure of the species as such remains unchanged. The life of an organism, in the course of its development, can be of longer or shorter duration than the average; death will always terminate it, however. For death is that inevitable phase of the recurrent changes of the species which completes the cycle, begun at birth, by reverting to the starting point.

The process which represents nothing more than procuring food to a hungry animal is killing to the prospective victim. In combat, the victory of the one is the defeat of the other. An operation, the normal working function of the surgeon and a part of his daily routine, may be a crucial event in the life of a patient. The transmutation of an egg into a caterpillar, a chrysalis, and a butterfly may be regarded as part of a vital function or as a transitional phase of evolution, depending on whether it is considered in the light of an individual or of the species. Similarly, the career of the individual human being within the community may be classified differently, according to the frame of reference under consideration.

For the clouds and their respective molecules, rain and lightning represent structural changes; for the earth, however, they are merely sections of a recurrent change. The transformations occurring on the earth's surface, such as hydrocirculation, ablation, stratification, diagenesis, and metamorphosis, being but recurrent changes of the globe, are yet structural changes for the molecules, crystals, and the rock.

The recurrent functions of a commercial enterprise or a population often enough mean evolutionary processes to the individual members. Generally speaking, *recurrent changes seem to be ultimately resolvable into structural changes, if ever smaller component elements are taken into account.*

CHAPTER II

THE CONCEPT OF THE SELF-MAINTAINING SYSTEM

1. *Definition of the Self-maintaining System*

Only a small number of examples have been picked out to elucidate the recurrent changes and the structural changes. The total of these phenomena is infinitely greater, so that it can never be exhausted. Thus we actually arrive at the following decisive statement: *In nature there are none but recurrent and structural changes.* There probably is no event or process which, provided that it is considered in relation to the appropriate frame of reference, is not part of a recurrent or a structural change.

Any regulatory system by itself, or self-maintaining system, and, in specific cases, the object, commodity, organism, the living being, man, the atom, molecule, crystal, etc., furnishes an appropriate and individual frame of reference, endowing the concepts of both the recurrent changes and the structural changes with a specific sense. Self-maintaining or self-regulatory natural systems are synonymous to steady-state systems. Self-maintaining systems are autonomous, self-regulating physical fields or entities. Making use of extreme simplification, we may state that these systems, fields, or entities operate according to the well-known feedback or closed-loop control. For instance, when driving a car at a constant speed, it is necessary to keep an eye on the speedometer, thus closing the loop: accelerator➤ motor➤ speedometer➤ driver➤ accelerator. The same general principle is involved in any thermostatic control, in running trains according to timetables, in the fluctuations of population in a given territory, in steam engines, in homeostasis, in the carbon cycle of our sun, in trade winds, in eddies, in electron movements around the nucleus, in biologic growth control, and so forth.*

The self-maintaining system generally occupies a limited and temporally variable space, the confines of which may be accessible to energy as well as matter. The extreme case in which energy and substance are not exchanged represents a closed system. The confines of the self-maintaining system, even if similar to pulsating soap bubbles that may continually alter their shape and position, will always enclose a specific state of organization. From the viewpoint of a self-maintaining system, disorder, instability, and the random element rule beyond its confines, and order, stability, and lawfulness govern within. The confines of a self-maintaining system are transgressible, shutting out nothing; they are of a fictitious nature and enclose merely a definite and peculiar state of organization or of "order."

The recurrent changes are in no sense merely additional or casual conjoint symptoms of the self-maintaining system; on the contrary, the recurrent changes endow them with their specific features. These alone enable us to recognize the existence and nature of the self-maintaining system. Furthermore, the recurrent changes determine the self-maintaining system's confines, which may be recognized by virtue of the recurrent changes only, thus representing the system's total field of force. Now we are able exactly to define the concept of the self-maintaining systems as used by us: *self-maintaining systems represent all those structures that are carriers or vehicles of recurrent changes, i.e. of circular causation.*

One might feel inclined to forego so complicated an explanation and to content oneself with less involved state-

---

* The essential principle of the self-maintaining system — like the broad class of automatic control systems — involves that the departure of the controlled quantity from the required average value is caused to change the controlled quantity so as to reduce the error. There is always a closed sequence involved, the sequence error-output-error, and the existing error must bring about its own reduction. This we term "negative feedback."

ments. Thus it would be possible to define, say, an apple, as characterized by constant spherical consistency of substance. Such statements which, in special cases, might suffice for the identification of certain objects cannot, however, be generalized, being insufficient or unsuitable in others, for consistency of substance and constancy of shape are not universal characteristics. A river, for instance, is continually changing its substance no less than a flame or an organism. Besides, a flame, like a swarm of bees or gnats, is perpetually changing its shape too, and an electromagnetic field or Schrödinger's probability entity ψ have neither substance nor shape. The fixed pole within the eternal fluctuation of phenomena is solely the recurrent changes. They also endow the self-maintaining system with their integrity and their existence.* They are the support any contemplation of nature clings to, even if unconsciously.

So in nature there actually is an immense multitude of "fields," spatially limited and temporally variable, within which any real event may be split up into two components, viz., recurrent changes and structural components, the former being of a conservative, the latter of a dynamic nature. These individual systems or fields, with everything they comprise, are defined as self-maintaining systems, and include objects, structures, forms, systems, things, limbs, organs, organisms, persons, states, atoms, stars, and so on. The self-maintaining systems themselves generally are again composed of elements likewise in the nature of self-maintaining systems, thus forming a universal gradational or hierarchical order. This means that any individual part of a self-maintaining system represents a self-maintaining system, but of a different order. The whole universe apparently breaks down into self-maintaining systems of different organization and complexity, each with its own unique properties of structure and behavior, held together by interwoven recurrent and structural changes.

The different branches of the natural sciences have to deal with a variety of self-maintaining systems: astronomy

---

* In wave-mechanics, for instance, we make use of so-called "self-consistent fields."

with stars and cosmic clouds, geophysics with the earth, physics with atoms, chemistry with molecules, crystallography with crystals, biology with organisms, geology with the upper layers of the terrestrial crust, stones, and rocks, national economy with trade and commerce, sociology with communities, technology with such commodities as machines, apparatus, instruments, tools, and so on. As the relations enumerated here concern the self-maintaining system as such without preference for any group, we may amalgamate the entire range of natural sciences into one entity, in any place and at any time obeying the same fundamental principles.

We are now able to state that *the universe is inhabited by nothing but self-maintaining systems,* and that nothing exists that is not a part of a self-maintaining system or not composed of self-maintaining systems.* This universal claim of totality establishes a connecting link between physics and biology as well as between astronomy and sociology. Insofar as they relate to the concepts of the recurrent changes, structural changes, and self-maintaining systems, there is no basic difference between the objects of physics and those of biology.

2. *The Objective and the Subjective Points of View*

All the examples quoted attest to the fact that the classification of real events into recurrent changes and structural changes is of a relative value and only valid in respect to a definite frame of reference. The self-maintaining system represents the frame of reference and may be characterized by contrasting it, as the "subject," with the "objects" of the surrounding medium or environment. If the object under observation, i.e. the "subject," is changed, different physical processes are revealed, and we may, therefore, indeed speak of a "physics of the subjective."

Recurrent changes and structural changes are mostly sections of a complex event. The recurrent changes re-establish,

---

* Elevating this equivalence of all coordinate systems—represented by self-maintaining systems—to a universal principle, we arrive at the general theory of relativity. The nonrigid self-maintaining systems are equivalent to Gaussian four-dimensional coordinate systems subjected to periodical transformation.

as already expounded, the initial situation of a self-maintaining system. And only that part of the event serving this aim alone belongs certainly to a recurrent change. Considering another self-maintaining system the partial processes are also differently grouped. Thus it happens that a certain partial process belongs to the recurrent changes of one self-maintaining system, while in another system it is part of the structural changes, depending upon which is under observation. So we take into account all the phenomena that relate to a "subject" serving as a reference system, and evaluate them first, disregarding farther-reaching causes and consequences, perhaps, which are energetically connected with them, but which occur outside the space-time section occupied by the "subject."

Studying the life of a bacillus, we first disregard any possible disaster connected with the outbreak of epidemics, as it does not directly affect either the recurrent or the structural changes of the bacillus. The regeneration of the oxygen used in breathing is not regarded as part of the process of respiration, although it is an inevitable prerequisite thereof. The subjective method of contemplation thus already claiming its right is the only obvious way of considering an individual's own affairs. Every system, from his point of view, first merely sees but one aspect of the matter; his horizon extends no further than the limital conditions.

The relation between subject and object depends upon the ability of the "observer" to assume the role of the "observed." Most obstacles to true knowledge arise from the unwillingness of the "observer" to accept the viewpoint of the "observed," even for a brief period of time. The deeper significance in such a procedure, however, must be sought in the fact that the immediate causes of the events or the actuating forces — metaphorically speaking, the motives and actions — are of a subjective nature, that the objective merely results from the subjective, and that *the subjective aspect of natural phenomena must be accorded priority in any contemplation of the same,* if the question whether anything occurs, and what it is that occurs, is to be answered.

Here the question arises whether the structural changes, by a suitable choice of the "subject," should be after all regarded as parts of recurrent changes. Such, however, does not appear to be the case, for a twofold reason. In the first place, any process in which many molecules are involved represents an increase of entropy, that is to say, an irreversible alteration of the cosmos which must appear somewhere in nature as genuine structural change. Second, the history of the evolution of organisms, of stars, and of atoms enables us to recognize irreversible structural changes. The genealogy of animals reveals an evolution of a singleness of tendency which can hardly be extended into a cyclic process. In the organism the hereditary and environmental properties seem liable to induce genuine structural changes, generally termed mutations. The expanding universe, the evolution of stars and of atoms, and the periodic system all suggest something analogous. At any rate, there seems to exist a real possibility of structural changes generating new species which exclude a repetition of the old. It is still beyond our imagination that, starting from man, the genealogy of the animals could ever again evolve in a backward direction.

3. Self-maintaining Systems and the Increase of Entropy

Self-maintaining systems are not closed systems in a thermodynamic sense, as their confines allow of a continual flux of energy and matter in either direction. The changes of entropy of the internal space and of the external space of a self-maintaining system are apparently indistinguishably interlaced. We mention only the process of human nourishment, in which it is difficult to say when exactly the food passes the boundary of the body.

A certain order, however, may be established even with regard to the most complicated internal and external interrelations, if processes progress cyclically, i.e. if after a certain period a former condition is repeatedly restored.* In such a

---

* A revealing analysis of system behavior is given by A. Tustin in his book: *The Mechanism of Economic Systems*, Harvard, 1953.

case, disregarding all intermediate stages, it is possible indeed by a comparison of the final condition with the initial state of the same phase to draw a balance, thus eliminating many complications that have ultimately canceled one another out.

Recurrent changes provide the theoretical foundation for the establishing of an energy balance, as the recurrent changes always revert to the initial state of the self-maintaining system, if only a suitable period of time is selected. The individual cycles are synchronal, revealing ever-constant effective values, and *the increase of entropy produced by recurrent changes is constant and independent of time.* The self-maintaining systems, at any rate, cause an increase of entropy which will amount to the same value within each period.

Structural changes are of a twofold significance for the increase of entropy. First, they change the constant intensity of the recurrent changes, and second, they transform the free energy of self-maintaining systems. These two effects are not independent of each other, the intensity of the recurrent changes depending one way or another upon the free energy of the self-maintaining system. This dependence is of a nature to involve an increase in the self-maintaining system's free energy, mostly, and is accompanied by intensification or acceleration of its recurrent changes.

As expounded, a constant intensity or velocity of increase in entropy is associated with the recurrent changes. This value of velocity varies with structural changes; that is to say, it increases or decreases. A structural change, therefore, is identical with an acceleration or retardation of the velocity or intensity of the increase in entropy. Therefore, from a physical point of view, the two phenomena mean something quite different, a fact demanding their distinction at any time and everywhere in nature.

Any structural change presupposes recurrent changes. This in particular means that there is no possibility of development, evolution, and death without metabolism, or of wear and tear and wastage without some recurrent changes.

The independence of recurrent changes from time itself, including their energy consumption, has been pointed out. Structural changes, however, are connected directly to time, or, rather, time is routed to actual things and events by structural changes. It follows, then, that without structural changes, i.e. without uniqueness, chance, or indeterminateness, there is no space-time universe; there could exist only the "eternal now" of *Euclidean* space.

4. *The Complementary Processes*

Considering all the infinitesimal transformations of energy appertaining not only directly but also indirectly to the recurrent changes, we notice countless influences taking a share in the process that are temporally and spatially remote from, yet dependent upon, one another. Think only of the activities of a farmer, including metabolism, tillage, harvesting, supply and preparation of food, shopping, transport, and so on, and it immediately becomes evident that recurrent changes do not constitute independent processes. All these activities are necessary complements to recurrent changes. In our proceedings so far we have isolated the recurrent changes by selecting only those which occur in a well-defined interval of space-time occupied by the self-maintaining system.

In order to obtain a firm basis for a more theoretical treatment of the complementary processes it seems to be advantageous to proceed from a physical example. We arrive at conditions familiar to us if we consider the unbroken succession of the identical cyclic processes of a periodically functioning machine of maximum efficiency whose sole object is the lowering of a load and the generating of heat. After the expiration of a period or a cycle, the initial situation of the machine is regained, but, mark, of the machine only, not of the surrounding medium or environment. Every cyclic process leaves some trace or causes a change in the surrounding medium. In this instance, a load has been lowered and heat has been accumulated. Therefore, before the next or any other subsequent cycle can start under the same conditions as the first, the changes effected in the surrounding medium must be eliminated, i.e. the initial conditions of the environment of the machine must, like those of the machine itself, be re-established.

A clock set in motion by a weight must be wound up by lifting the weight again if it is to keep going. In this example, too, heat generated by friction must be absorbed and removed by the atmosphere. To understand the working of a machine it is immaterial whether the special method of restitution inclusive of the environment is known or not. It is quite sufficient to know that there is some device insuring the machine of a constant supply of free energy and seeing to the removal of the expended energy. In our particular case it is necessary that the clock should at all times be provided with an adequately lifted weight and a medium of suitable temperature to absorb and remove the heat produced by every new cycle.

For its manner of working and the drawing up of a balance thereof, the kind of mechanism used for winding the clock and the method of removing the heat generated by its working are of no consequence. The regeneration of the environment, i.e. of the working conditions after one or more cycles of the machine, may take place in a variety of ways. Which way it actually takes place, however, is of no direct importance for a self-maintaining system of this type; for the working of a machine it seems to be quite immaterial in what manner the fuel is supplied and the converted energy disposed of.

The above statements, as exemplified by the cyclic processes of machines working periodically, are valid in principle for all the recurrent changes of any self-maintaining system whatever. In this sense, man and the other living organisms are periodic operating machines capable of continuing their particular kind of existence provided that their recurrent changes meet with the required complements in their environment. And yet, any actual consideration of the system proper disregards those necessary complementary processes in the environment.

A parasite, to mention another instance, does not inquire into the origin of its victims or into their sufferings. The host-organism, the existence of which in its environment the parasite assumes as given, is nothing but a vital condition for it. A cow kept as a domestic animal must be fed and milked. Whether the milking, the necessary external complementary process to its vital functions, is performed by a calf, by human hands, or by an electrical apparatus is fundamentally of no material importance to the cow.

Further examples are the management of a hotel, a public transport service, or any public institution, all of which presuppose a number of customers with particular demands. Moreover, there are the vital functions of the honey-seeking insects in quest of honey-yielding blossoms complementing those of the plants dependent upon the pollinating insects. Similarly, the recurrent changes of the atoms and molecules of the atmosphere are contingent upon external mechanisms, viz. the activity of the sun emitting light and heat, which we disregard when inquiring into the atom-physical processes within the separate individual systems.

The interconnection existing between recurrent changes and their complementary processes in the surrounding medium, as expounded above in regard to machines and organisms, is of still greater moment for all commodities and structures such as transmission gears and the like, which by reason of external processes suffer their recurrent changes passively. Commodities depend upon a producer and a user if they are to undergo recurrent changes and take their place in the steady routine of life.

Structural changes are also complemented from without, and any change in the structure of a self-maintaining system is accompanied by a structural change in its environment. Any change in the working intensity of the machine is associated with a corresponding change in the supply of free energy and the removal of degraded energy. For example, the working intensity of an electric motor changes together with the current introduced from without and the external tension. The growth and ageing of an animal results in an altered consumption of food and a changed power of external activity. An alteration in his environment also influences man's way of life. His mode of living changes concomitantly with his economic position and his income, while he may, conversely, also gain or lose his income and position within his environment by his activity. A structural change in commodities will likewise change their exploitable value.

Any self-maintaining system is ever forming its environment by recurrent changes, just as, on the other hand, the surrounding medium is ever molding the self-maintaining system; *both inseparably belong together.* The interplay which manifests itself is such that any structural change in the one will influence and affect the other. Although the structural changes are always necessarily associated with changes in the complementary processes, we do not include the changes of these processes in our concept of the structural changes. The forces and reasons which cause and motivate the killing of an animal make no difference to the animal itself. The increase of metabolism which forms an essential part of man's vital functions is included in his growth, but not the increase of the store of food and oxygen in his environment. What is valid for structural changes is also valid for recurrent changes; both of necessity possess an obverse in their surrounding medium which is not included in the concept of those changes.

In our discussion we have applied ideas which can be extended from a periodically functioning machine of maximum efficiency to any self-maintaining system whatever, ranging from commodities to human communities. By this we maintain the universal validity not only of our results but also of our entire chain of reasoning from the very beginning. Instead of the periodically functioning machine, we might have selected any other of the items enumerated to serve as an example for our explanations, yet we should always have arrived at the same conclusion.

5. *Remarkable Relations between Self-maintaining Systems and Their Environment*

We have revealed the fact that the functioning of our machine is bound up with certain external conditions within the surrounding medium or environment. These conditions are not absolutely constant, for they must always be restored, being changed—at least temporally—by every cyclic process. In order to insure a succession of such cyclic processes, they must be complemented in the surrounding medium by parallel processes. Even though irreversible processes can never lead to absolutely completed cyclic processes, we nevertheless obtain, by virtue of the complementary processes, closed cyclic processes within the space occupied by the self-maintaining system.

Thus we have to deal with *two parallel mechanisms harmonizing with each other* and consisting of a continual succession of cyclic processes remote from each other: first, the working of the machine, and second, an external mechanism responsible for the maintenance of the working conditions. The working of the machine differs from the external mechanism insofar as it occurs in a well-defined space-time section. In spite of the contiguity and interdependence of the recurrent changes with the complementary processes in the environment, we discriminate between their concepts for two reasons. In the first place, a variety of complementary processes may belong to one and the same recurrent change, so that their assumed absence only will create discernible conditions; and, second, a balance of entropy (and of free energy) can be based on nothing but recurrent changes.

The expediency of a distinction between recurrent changes on the one hand, and their complementary processes in the environment on the other, results primarily from the fact that the two kinds of processes are isolated in space and in time by definite limits, represented by the confines of the self-maintaining system and thus being entirely independent of each other in essential points. We have to deal, in a manner of speaking, with two halves of one whole which must fit where they touch, but which may, in energetical respects, be of any nature whatever. These halves must complement each other as regards the exchange of substance and energy at the point of their contiguity only, being in all other respects quite independent of each other not only in their specific nature but also in their power to increase entropy. Turning back once more to the example of a periodically functioning machine, as treated of above, the supply of fuel and the disposal of the output need not be associated with an increase of entropy at all, much less with any definite amount of the same. For the working of the machine, only two limital conditions must be maintained, which may be accomplished in an infinite variety of ways.

The fact that a definite increase of entropy or an equivalent depreciation of energy is a property of recurrent changes but not of their complementary processes is by no means the only difference separating recurrent changes from complementary processes. Another distinction consists in the fact that *recurrent changes are limited to the space occupied by the self-maintaining system whereas its complementary process need not be limited at all in space and time.* A clock wound up by having its weight lifted, for instance, can be wound up by a different person each time, just as the removal of the heat produced may take place in any direction and to any distance whatever. The oxygen essential to the respiratory process of animals may be generated in any way, in any place, and conveyed at any time: the respective complementary process is not tied to any definite moment or plant. The limital conditions to be observed merely require that the oxygen be conveyed to the respiratory organ.

Frequently, the complementary processes of recurrent changes are inseparable from some other self-maintaining systems. This gives rise to organismal communities where the recurrent changes of one self-maintaining system simultaneously constitute the complementary processes of the other. Such communities are the family, symbiosis, parasitism, animal communities, and particularly ant hills, termitaries, beehives, coral, herds, flocks, and cell colonies.

Solar systems, twin stars, molecules, atoms and their nuclei, crystals, forests, plant communities and biocoenoses, possibly are all formed and molded according to the same basic principle. Let us consider the following example.

Modern life — with its extended and very complex system of communication, which includes radio, television, telephone, travel, airplanes, newspapers, movies; with polluted and contaminated water and air, chemically treated foods, drugs—constantly is molding our brain and body. Headlines, myths, propaganda, and beliefs are conditioning governments and people. We have to consider this intricate system of technology and communication that now encloses the whole of earth as complementary to our body and sense organs, linking up about every individual. Obviously some new kind of semitechnical organism, a symbiosis between man and machine, is evolving.

At the end of the chapter we summarize:

The concept of self-maintaining system has been successfully introduced to describe relativistically a system that is

a) elementary in the sense that it no longer can be decomposed into more elementary sub-systems or constituents without losing its individual characteristics, but is

b) so substantial, nevertheless, as to be able to contain a variety of sub-systems (constituents, particles) with different characteristics.

Chapter III

RESULTS

1. *The System Concept of Evolution*

Our procedure so far might give rise to the objection that the kind of energy balance we have drawn up with regard to the self-maintaining systems and their environments is without objective value, for our procedure has been based on the subjective concepts or recurrent and structural changes enjoying no independent existence of their own but depending upon complementary processes. Having disregarded these complementary processes occurring in the surrounding medium of the self-maintaining system, our balance seems consequently to be incomplete and incorrect.

Our balance is quite intentionally limited to a finite, well-defined space, viz. the space occupied by a self-maintaining system. Even though the forces within the confines of a self-maintaining system transgress into the outer world and interact with it, yet the recurrent and the structural changes deducted from the subjective phenomena are limited to the space-time section occupied by the self-maintaining system and independent of the increase of entropy effected in any other way. Should our balance, roughly speaking, appear incomplete, it nevertheless is complete as regards any space-time section occupied by a self-maintaining system. Therefore the amounts of entropy resulting from this kind of balance are closely connected with scalar magnitudes of a temporally variable space-time section. The self-maintaining systems are, so to speak, energetically homogeneous units or fields with quite definite powers for increasing entropy. By assembling all these units we obtain a complete representation of the increase in entropy of the entire universe.

We must conclude that there are in nature a very large number of parallel levels or of tracks, each characterized by a definite velocity or intensity of increase in entropy. Each self-maintaining system is chained to a certain level by strength of its recurrent changes, and moves on this level only. If the self-maintaining system is to be represented by a point in a system of co-ordinates, time having been marked on its abscissa and the rate of increase of entropy on its ordinate, the point will proceed parallel to the abscissa. Progressive or retrogressive tendencies seek to lift or lower the self-maintaining system to another level, simultaneously accomplishing structural changes, a process which is associated with an acceleration or retardation of the otherwise steady increase of entropy.

In spite of the close interaction and conjunction of the two basic processes, the stationary or conservative events can at any time and in any place be separated from the dynamic events. This being done, the result provides quite a novel and fascinating picture of nature and its forces, and a new basis for fundamental research and insight. Those able to visualize this picture will see something as beautiful as a work of art created by a painter, and obtain at the same time a deeper insight into nature's workings than is possible from a mere survey of outward appearance.

The actual course of natural evolution, as becomes manifest in natural history, points to a tendency ever to extend to the utmost the integral of the increase of entropy or of energy degradation in time and space. The self-maintaining systems insure this high integral value. Accordingly, it is not the purpose of the self-maintaining systems to dissipate as much energy as possible at a given time, that is to say, to radiate especially intensive energy or vitality. If such were the case, we should do well to burn up coal, wood, petroleum, and release atomic energy, and the like, all at once, even though such a procedure would victimize all the organisms. The purpose seems to be rather to insure the *utmost duration of the utmost degradation of energy,* that is to say, to insure the utmost duration of the utmost intensity of organic and inorganic metabolism, i.e. of life and order.

However, the attainment of a maximum integral value demands first of all an *expedient utilization* and accumulation of the free energy available. Such an expedient economizing and accumulation of free energy is provided by the self-maintaining systems. Examples are our radiant sun and living organisms. Both are continuously degrading their energies as efficiently as possible under the prevailing circumstances, and are simultaneously maintaining their individual organization. We may observe something similar in a person or a nation who does not use up his reserves of money, raw material, or other commodities, but keeps them in order to work with the maximum possible productivity. The conjecture would still be possible that the ultimate aim of evolution is the economizing and accumulation of free energy, that is to say, a slowing down of the increase of entropy, thus increasing "negative entropy."

The independent origin and development of organisms or of organic life rather mislead us to the conclusion that the increase of entropy is retarded by the activity of the organisms and the accompanying generation of free energy. The view that the increase of entropy progresses more slowly in the organic than in the inorganic, or is even negative, has indeed been maintained. That such is not possible becomes evident from a complete balance in which not only the change in the entropy of the organism is included in the calculation, but the recurrent changes, as well as the complementary processes, are considered. The comparatively inconsiderable local decrease of entropy, which is equivalent to a local accumulation of free energy or to a certain quantity of local negative entropy, generally constitutes only the inauguration of new and intensive processes of dissipation. Under normal conditions, the accumulation of energy formed in this way is finally again dissipated.

The recurrent changes of our planet do not alter its structure, all changes being merely phasic changes which have been canceled out at the expiration of each period. In this way, recurrent changes maintain pulsating life all over the world. But according to the second law of thermodynamics, they must involve an increase of entropy, thus being incapable of an isolated existence. Recurrent changes are inevitably accompanied by structural changes that must necessarily manifest themselves somewhere. The structural changes irreversibly transform the appearance of the earth's surface; and more, they are the reason for the fact that our globe knows historical events and exhibits a tradition. Similarly to all the self-maintaining systems known to us, such as stars, organisms, atoms, and molecules, the earth displays an historical evolution which is the subject of scientific research aimed at furnishing us with information about the unique phenomena of the past, the present, and the future.

The structural changes resulting from recurrent changes do not just represent an indifferent alteration of the universe. On the contrary, the rate of entropic increase is raised or lowered by the structural changes, representing progression or regression in the advance toward the ultimate cosmic aim. In this way, every change in nature acquires physically well-determined and definable values.

2. *The Unified System Pattern of the Universe*

The individual human being finds himself in association with his like, and he represents — as one might say — only an elementary unit of the community to which he belongs. The social bonds and relations and ties that he feels represent the external relational pattern surrounding him. These external relations experienced personally are but tiny fragments of the entire *internal* relational pattern of the community. The real nature of the interwoven internal relationship forming the community, as well as the external or outwardly directed exercise of national power, are things which the average citizen only comes to know by long and devious detours. Although the individual is carried by the community in which he lives, the community itself remains highly unsurveyable so long as the individual is not personally and directly involved by common destiny, as, for instance, in times of war, revolution, and economic depression. This little example, comprehensible to all of us, gives perhaps an idea about the relational pattern, if the terms "social relations," "association," "love," "ties" are replaced by complementary processes, and the individual by "self-maintaining system."

A majority of the so-called things that surround us have a certain relational pattern, but mostly this pattern has been formed secondarily by man himself and fitted into the pattern of specific use. Natural structures and systems that intrude in our lives, such, for instance, as climate, the beauties of nature, local topography, mountains and woods, a waterfall, wild animals, or even a grain of sand in our eye, generally represent but mere fragments or parts of larger systems from which they proceed as subordinated features. To gain a more complete view, we have, therefore, to look for the principal systems and to study their arrangement and interrelation within the whole of nature.

We observe that the world is built from different classes of individual systems that are connected with each other by a very peculiar interlaminated relational pattern. For example, the external relations of the so-called elementary particles (electrons, neutrons, protons, mesons, and so on) constitute the internal relations of atomic nuclei and of atoms; the external relations of atoms constitute the internal relations of molecules; the external relations of molecules constitute the internal relations of macromolecules and of crystals; the external relations of crystals constitute the internal relations of minerals; the external relations of minerals constitute the internal relations of geologic or petrographic bodies; the external relations of these bodies constitute the internal relations of the earth's crust including the ocean; the external relations of the earth's crust constitute the internal relations of the whole planet (or at least a part of it), including the biosphere and the atmosphere; the external relations of earth and of other analogous celestial bodies constitute the internal relations of the solar system; the external relations of the solar system constitute the internal relations of our galactic system; and, finally, the external relations of the galactic system constitute the internal relations of a galactic supersystem or, at least, of a substantial part of the known universe.*

Every level or stratum within the universal hierarchy of individual systems may be compared to a great multitude of individual pieces of stone, wood, glass, and such things, of different color, structure, and shape, inlaid to form a grandiose mosaic design. Of course, there are fluctuations, changes, and unpredictable events, which constantly create opportunities for new organization and order, but in spite of the heterogeneous versatility of systems and events, the basic pattern remains permanent. The principal characteristic of the pattern is the continuous gradation of individual systems according to conception: "element"➤ "system"➤"element"➤"system" ➤ and so on. The gradation has its own direction with appurtenant contrast of direction, as, for instance, that of the "higher" and the "lower" stages of organization, or that of the "superordinated" and the "subordinated" systems. This contrast of direction has, moreover, the nature of convergent numerical series, of which we humans can observe and recognize a small section only, and that but imperfectly. This peculiar graded succession of interlaminated systems represents the ordinal progression of a dimension quite different from the space-time dimensions we are using today in physics.

The relational interdependence of individual systems is reflected in a very impressive way by the horizontal and vertical extension of "isomorphic" laws in nature. Isomorphic laws represent formally identical mathematical formu-

---

* The largest self-maintaining system known to us represents the whole universe, if "continuous creation" is assumed. The smallest self-maintaining systems probably are the atomic nuclei and their individual constituents.

lations which may apply to many different fields of science. Horizontal isomorphism is structural identity and vertical isomorphism is the application of laws to different levels of organization. The well-known exponential law, for instance, which expresses decay and growth, may be applied to any self-maintaining system independently of the nature of that system. Some examples are radioactive decay, the killing rate of bacteria by disinfectants, the loss of body-substance in starvation, the discharge of a storage battery, the cooling of hot bodies, and, on the other hand, the heating of an atomic pile, the increase of radiation of an exploding star, the individual growth of organisms and the growth of a population, the growth curve of scientific papers and inventions, or the growth of the chemical industry in the United States. Incidentally, all the structural changes we have been discussing may also be represented by the exponential function applied in statistics and in probability calculus.

Much new theoretical and practical knowledge is also based on the proper application of isomorphic laws. We mention here only a few: the unitarian field theory of Einstein; the study of communication; the servomechanisms and feedback systems of Norbert Wiener and his associates, including the role of cybernetics in physiology; the homeostasis concept of W. B. Cannon; Toynbee's doctrine of recurrence in history; the general system theory of L. von Bertalanffy in theoretical biology and its application to nonbiological systems; the modern theory of turbulence dealing with the hierarchy of eddies and its extension to the motion of galaxies by the well-known astrophysicist G. Gamow; the thermodynamics of open reaction systems; and the increasing role of mathematical statistics in practically every field of learning.

In terminating the first part, let us express the main findings by a brief definition: *The universe is a strata-system composed of individual self-maintaining systems or oscillating fields of singularities. A special gradational pattern, resulting from the complementary processes of the two basic processes we have termed recurrent and structural changes, links to-*

gether and integrates all the individual systems, fields or entities of different strata, thus forming the complete super-system of heterogeneous versatility we term "universe." Every individual unit simultaneously reflects internal and external relations. Internal relations are reflected if the system is viewed as a whole, and external relations are reflected if the individual component elements of the same system are to be considered. Therefore every individual entity represents a perfect whole and at the same time an assembly or a community of ever smaller and smaller subclasses or individual subordinated entities.

The structural changes only are equivalent to time, for time does not exist in a changeless, frictionless, or abstractly mechanical universe, in a world without any structural changes. In the first chapter it has been pointed out that it seems to be quite unlikely for a very complex system, our universe, to exist without random elements, since indeterminateness alone could furnish the necessary flexibility of nature in order to cope with unavoidable defects and keep things running smoothly. A changeless, and therefore time-less, universe, an eternal recurrence devoid of imagination, is a purely abstract concept without any reality. Actually nature has freshness, novelty, and uniqueness of change, in addition to the dependability of circular causation.

PART TWO

THE ORGANIC IMAGE

Chapter I

THE FITNESS OF ORGANIC ACTIVITIES

1. *The Fitness of the Organic*

It is a generally established fact that the events of nature perceptible to our senses are not an uncontrollable sequence of isolated occurrences, a confused disorder of unsystematic activity, nor the mere play of disconnected transformations; they are, rather, processes obeying rules and laws which somehow connect and make everything existing interdependent. The fact that our brain expects the frequently experienced sequence of cause and effect to be true in respect to future events also is causality, or causation, connecting causes and effects, reasons and consequences.

The cause-effect habit of the human mind provides, even today, the foundation upon which physics — in the widest sense of the word — bases its conclusions and prognostications, and deduces rules and laws.* It is established for us beyond doubt that the movement of a celestial body or of a stone dropping to earth is caused by forces directly acting upon it. Therefore we also try either to discover the existing fields of energy or the governing law from its behavior, or to infer the latter from the former. Not so in biology, how-

---

* Max Planck, the founder of the quantum theory, writes: "The principle of causality must be held to extend even to the highest achievements of the human soul. We must admit that the mind of each one of our great geniuses — Aristotle, Kant or Leonardo, Goethe or Beethoven, Dante or Shakespeare— even at the moments of its highest flights of thought or in the most profound inner workings of his soul — was subject to the causal fiat and was an instrument in the hands of an almighty law which governs the world" (quoted from J. Jeans, *Physics and Philosophy*).

ever. Here quite a new and different movement appears, which proves indispensable for the investigation of living beings. All the same, there is no reason to doubt that in biology events are determined by forces acting in accordance with physics. In many respects, biology successfully bases its work on these, especially in the spheres of physiology and genetics, morphology, histology, cytology, and the like. However, if these were the only facts upon which to base our biological observations of nature, our knowledge concerning living organisms would not be extensive, as here all the conditions are somewhat intricate and obscure. We do not know even today what are the forces active in mitosis, and what physicochemical impulse an animal is obeying when it attacks its enemy, builds its nest, seeks a sexual partner, or, like the caterpillar, turns into a chrysalis. And yet we are able, in many cases, to predict, judge, and understand the behavior of organisms.

The peculiar fitness of organic activities reveals to us the fact that organic events seem to possess a purpose, that they are directed toward an aim, or that, to all appearances, a definite design or pattern underlies these processes. When a swallow, a stickleback, or a water spider builds an elaborate nest, something serving a future purpose occurs, namely, the preparation of a receptacle for the eggs or the spawn. In acting thus, animals behave in a manner which is apparently determined not only by actual impulses, but also by the future aim. The latter, at least, furnishes us with more information as to the observed behavior than do the directly active forces of causality, which are mostly unknown to us.

Migratory birds flying south to warmer weather, in autumn, provide by their action against the approaching cold of winter. Here, too, behavior appears to be controlled by an event in the future. Very instructive in this connection is the behavior of the male stag-beetle larva, which provides in good time a space in the wood for the big mandibles peculiar to the male. The manifold precautionary measures subservient to the interests of their progeny that living creatures take are especially striking. Think only of the murderous sand wasp (*ammophila sabulosa*) laying its eggs in other animals, and of the winged seeds of certain plants, "flying apparatus" so cunningly produced as to insure the widest possible propagation. These facts are, however, sufficiently common property to warrant our refraining from a detailed enumeration.

The fitness of organic activities enables us to study the behavior of animals even in cases where causality fails us. This does not mean that the inorganic should not be expedient also. To be sure, the sun, rain, and the alternation of day and night are, on the whole, fitting for us. A house, a bridge, a machine, and in fact all commodities, are after all, purposeful for us; for all these things were actually designed by an architect, inventor, or engineer with a definite plan and purpose, in accordance with which they were constructed, and which are the true reasons for their behavior. We will discuss later the essential difference between the inorganic and the organic. First we establish fitness as a principle existing side by side with causality and apparently independent of it. For the sake of completeness, be it mentioned that a third view is still possible, namely, the historical. This maintains its position in astronomy, geology, and, above all, in the history of mankind. Though not treating of the historical view in detail, we think it appropriate to allude to it in the interest of completeness.

If the sun is expedient for organisms, the sun is not itself the origin of such fitness. The fact that organisms have adapted themselves to their environment is the source of this fitness. It is the designer who is the source of the expediency of a machine or of certain commodities; that is to say, it is again an organism that produced these things. Although fitness is recognizable in the whole of nature, its source lies exclusively within the organisms. Therefore we may speak of inorganic fitness only in relation to living creatures, i.e. organisms.

The purpose which organisms are serving is to be found in themselves alone, while with regard to inanimate things we must look for the purpose outside of them and again in the realm of organisms. The behavior of an organism serves its own purpose or that of the community to which it belongs, thus in one way or another finally serving itself again. So there are definite boundaries between the animate and the inanimate, since alone the animate gives rise to fitness. If nature were deprived of all life, all fitness would disappear from the world. In order to fix the boundaries between the two spheres, some authors distinguish between a self-serving fitness and one serving others. A distinction of this kind, though possible, is not always easy to establish, and we therefore prefer to consider fitness proper as the criterion of life.

The terms, "living matter," "organic matter," "organism," thus imply structures which are a source or origin of fitness. An organism is animate because expedient structures and processes are traceable to it. Machines and commodities are inanimate because the origin of their fitness does not lie in themselves but is traceable to their designers. The sun, the earth, and the rain, as well as other natural phenomena, need not be animate because they are not the source of fitness. Those structures, rather, to which is traceable the fact that the sun, the rain, day and night, and other natural phenomena serve a certain purpose, are animate or alive, namely, the adaptable and adapted organisms. Thus we may formulate the following definition: *Every active or self-maintaining source of fitness is alive.*

The property of fitness may, therefore, serve as a criterion in delimiting the spheres of the animate and the inanimate. Man has always been able somehow to discriminate between these two, yet differences of opinion are possible. This is not surprising if we remember that a locomotive or a motorcar is often taken for a living being by a child or a savage. In order to exclude all error in this distinction, we should let ourselves be guided by some well-defined characteristic. Such an infallible maxim to rely upon in doubtful cases is fitness. Should it someday be proved, for instance, that some molecules, in their structure and function, possess the faculty of fitness, it would inevitably follow that they be classified as organisms — a contingency to be discussed later on.

In any case, we have reason to assume that the purpose aimed at by nature is in most cases not premeditated; it is attained purely automatically, rather, without any conscious intention on the part of the acting organism. Surely, the male stag-beetle larva does not provide the extra space for its future mandibles in consequence of well-considered, deliberate calculation. Even clever man is still ignorant of the ultimate purpose ordained for him by nature. It is a mysterious mechanism which sees to it that the influence of the environment in conjunction with inner tendencies ordains such a surprisingly far-reaching behavior in plants, animals, and, to a far greater extent still, in the human being — a behavior the ultimate aim of which seems to be the preservation of the generative faculty with a simultaneous evolution of the species. Calling it "instinct," we introduce a word devoid of any physical substratum, so that it does not supply the connecting link with physical systematology. In spite of this, as already mentioned, we may foretell the behavior of organisms, because their purpose and design are mostly known to us.

Analogous to the method adopted with regard to our own behavior, we are often guided by psychical concepts. Terms like "impulse," "activity," "natural necessity," or "desire," "instinct," "complex," and the like have an essentially psychical meaning. Therefore the method of orientation differs greatly in the two cases: in the one, we are searching for the cause, in the other, for the purpose, and in searching for the purpose we usually enter the province of psychology. In the following chapters we will attempt to base fitness upon a physical foundation.

2. Natural Selection

In organic nature we find a peculiar harmonious relation reigning in the coexistence of individuals, so that the individual organism appears adapted to the environment encompassing it. This natural process has been defined as adaptability and adaptation to the conditions of life and has been linked to the directiveness of organic activities or fitness. The question as to the nature of the principle has so far been answered by investigators in two ways.

One of these attempts to explain the nature of the principle consists merely in circumscribing it, tracing its origin to other indefinable phenomena — such as "impulse," "natural necessity," "inner causes" — of adaptation to external conditions and of evolution in a certain direction. The Frenchman Lamarck (1744-1829) may be regarded as the most prominent representative of this view. Lamarck quite correctly recognized the transforming influence of the environment. Lamarck's principle does not, however, suffice to explain the abundance of phenomena of adaptation, and as he was not yet acquainted with Darwin's theory of natural selection he introduced circumscriptive terms such as "natural necessity" and "impulse." This manifests itself rather plainly when Lamarck tries to explain the origin of new organs. Yet, granting every concession demanded by the Lamarckists in respect to their anthropomorphic view of organisms, it would be impossible to explain most of the so-called passive adaptations by this method. Up till now, we could choose whether to adopt the metaphysical view or explain this kind of adaptation by natural selection.

The only real attempt at a solution of this problem by searching for the existence of an organic fitness was made by Darwin (1809-1882) by demonstrating a causally explainable and actually existing selective influence of the environment, which insures lasting preservation through generations solely to adapted individuals by a constant elimination of all the less efficiently adapted.

In the past fifty years the foundation laid by Lamarck and Darwin has been constantly modified and complemented by genetics and its more recent experimental research. The heredity-versus-environment question has fascinated biologists ever since, but no generally convincing solution of the problem has yet emerged. We are, for instance, still very far from understanding how either heredity or environment influences intelligence, temperament, or other psychic traits.

The investigation of the basic units of heredity — the genes — has made far greater progress, and these powerful particles have occupied the center of the geneticist's interest. Results in this direction are the discrimination between the hereditariness and non-hereditariness of variations and mutations, and the realization that natural selection is capable only of isolating existing types, and not capable of creating new properties, whether qualitative or quantitative. Natural selection, therefore, is limited to a rather negative, if extraordinarily effective, activity, as it merely acts in the sense of sifting and conditioning. Does our complicated nervous system, the process of mitosis, i.e. division of cells, heredity, and consciousness, exist because of, or rather in spite of, selection? How these structures and processes could come into existence at all is a question still awaiting solution.

Great difficulty attaches to the task of determining the true relative influence of genotype and environment respectively, and it is here precisely that the opinions of biologists diverge widely. This dispute has been carried far beyond the boundaries of corporate science, and, in particular, sociologists, philosophers, historians, theologians, and politicians are now also concerned with these problems, since one of the fundamental theses of dialectical materialism — which finds its expression in current ideologies and doctrines — is based on an overestimation of the environmental influence. It must be added that, in contrast to this, there are also many who overestimate the purely genetic factor.

Modern concepts of adaption and selection are based chiefly on observation and deduction rather than actual experiments. The main reason for this is that evolution in higher animals is a very slow process, which cannot easily be seen in action. More recent studies of fruit-flies and of bacteria,* however, furnish some new experimental evidence to work upon, for bacteria have been observed through as many as ten thousand generations, which is the equivalent of about

---

* Experiments on bacteria conducted by Joshua Lederberg and his co-workers at the University of Minnesota.

250 thousand years of human evolution. The principal findings are very interesting, because they conform to the concept of recurrent and structural changes discussed in Part One:

1) Environmental changes may induce bacteria to evolve in any desired direction despite the randomness of the primary mutations. Resistance to penicillin, for instance, is inherited, and descendants will multiply either in the presence or the absence of this antibiotic. Penicillin-resistant strains of bacteria are taking the place of less resistant ones.

2) When an environment remains constant, bacteria evolve toward a better and better adjustment to that environment. Although mutations are reversible, one fitter type, which is always present among the preponderant parental bacteria, overgrows and eliminates all the other mutants. New mutants then occur among the fitter type, only to be eliminated likewise when types fitter than they appear. This steady progressive evolution constantly depresses the number of mutants and stabilizes the parental stock.

It is sometimes contended that mutations are not sufficient to provide the raw material for evolution, because mutations are usually considered harmful. The experiments with bacteria prove, however, that selection is a powerful force, and that it stabilizes and perpetuates those rare mutations that are actually given an advantage in the struggle for survival. The only possible change, even in an unchangeable environment, must be in the direction of adapting the parental stock to the environment. This kind of straight-line evolution may be observed in nature on a large scale in mammoths' tusks, which steadily became larger and larger.

To sum up, we have reason to believe that random mutations occurring in the chromosomes of cells constantly furnish the sensitive material of races or of populations, i.e. the opportunity, upon which the environmental energies are acting. This action is selective, neglecting certain mutations and favoring others. It thus conserves and improves the adaptive hereditary constitution and simultaneously maintains a safe residuum of other mutations in case intensive environmental changes call for new adaptive types. This whole process of mutation and selection, occurring in a population or a race, may be likened to a large photographic plate that is re-creating itself over and over again for the purpose of taking ever better and more efficient pictures of the environment.

CHAPTER II

THE CONCEPT OF THE ORGANIC IMAGE

1. *The Reaction of Organisms to Their Environment*

Any change in an organism, that is to say, all movements, processes, or functions occurring within a human organism or issuing from it, is the result of internal and external forces. All over the body are delicate receptors to pick up and partly decode the signal-patterns received from the environment. The sensory nerves are changed immediately upon irritation and its corresponding excitation. This change does not, however, disappear as soon as the irritation ceases, but dies down gradually, taking seconds or even minutes. Such after-effects have been observed not only in the more highly organized animals, but also in monoplasts and plants without a nervous system. The sensory nerves of the higher animals carry a continuous flow of electrical impulses or signal-patterns to the central nervous system from all parts of the body. Most information derived from environment comes by way of the sensations of sight, hearing, touch, taste, and smell, each of which has its own system of nerves. The information is transmitted by nerve fibers consisting of a chain of relay stations. The impulses have the amplitude characteristic of the nerve fiber they flow in and can vary only in frequency.

The energies capable of producing excitation and reaction include those of the slightest magnitude and are usually supported by vitamin, ferment, or hormone action, and the like. The death's-head moth (*noctuid*) in search of a female is led on by the most minute traces of odoriferous matter. The hawk, darting down upon its espied prey from a great height, is actuated by scarcely noticeable electromagnetic waves that strike its sharp eye and whose intensity is measurable only by the number of its energy quanta or photons. Directed by hardly discernible sense-perceptions, the forest animal, avoiding all collisions, finds its way unerringly to its desired objective. This disproportion betweeen cause and effect is still more evident in all kinds of technical magnifying apparatus. Thus the most insignificant differences in the light and sound waves of the spoken word evoke a variety of effects of the utmost consequence.

In these cases, the excited and reacting organic matter is not open to our observation at all, not to mention the fact that we cannot analyze the processes occurring here either through a microscope or by any other instrument and arrive at further conclusions. Who could say, judging from the slight energetic processes acting upon the skin or other peripheral sensory organs, what energy, what sense-impressions, or perceptions the animal in question receives, or who could predict its subsequent behavior?

It is nevertheless possible to examine and discuss the behavior of organisms and the laws governing that behavior since every organic process is governed by still another principle, namely, that of fitness, or purposiveness, as we have expounded in the first chapter. Organic behavior is mostly a means to a certain end, the knowledge of which enables us to formulate the necessary proposition for further conclusions. In other words, organic behavior follows a pattern, a template, or a design, and this pattern or design furnishes us with information about subsequent events. Even though we do not at first know either the pattern or its origin, we have the possibility of learning its nature as it manifests itself in the construction of organisms and their behavior within their environment.

Once we have discovered the design by observation, we are able to form all necessary conclusions, even with regard to the missing observations. For this design also includes the releasing processes within the peripheral sensory organs as connecting links in the complete event. Our understanding depends on the fact that organisms, although reacting to an immediate influence only and not to all external stimuli, create the impression that the attained result is based upon an ingenious design directed toward a distant future.

This obvious inherent singleness of purpose directed at a distant future affords an insight into the behavior of organisms, even if we disregard the peripheral conditions close to the body surface. As soon as we seek the purpose, aim, and design of the organisms, we at once perceive the reason why, for instance, the male stag-beetle larva makes a larger cavity in the wood than it needs at the time, and why it must behave thus. It is, therefore, the design that we must know in order to comprehend the behavior of individual organisms. We obtain this knowledge by observing their entire living-space, which may be more easily surveyed than the minute energetic transformations in the sensory organs on the surface of the body. The forces and energies of the environment become effective in a quite definite order, which stands in no relation to the remoteness in space and time.

Thus it is not only possible but even inevitable that the relations of organisms be discovered and their behavior systematized, with regard to their remoter surroundings, and this should be done, as is usually the case, by completely disregarding the subtle surficial processes. At best, the physiologist will pay attention to the processes at the peripheral sensory organs, although they include the surficial conditions so important for the behavior of organisms. Anyone else wishing to learn facts about the behavior of organisms will pass them over as too difficult to survey. Even the investigator who examines a biological problem like the vital habits of an animal, or, say, the fungous cultures of the leaf-cutter ant, will hardly deal with the energetic processes on the surface of the animal, although these actually determine the behavior of organisms. The author rather holds that the effect upon an organism is evoked by the entire environmental complex, physical, biological and social, which mainly concerns the ecologist.

The higher animal intelligently and harmoniously adapts

itself to the entire complex of environment and thus creates the impression that *the environment in its entirety is acting upon it.* By entirety the physicist must think of a space-time system of unity in the sense of Einstein and Minkowski.* The so-called alarm reaction of differently conditioned animals bears out this statement. The animal organism possesses a general defense mechanism that automatically mobilizes against any stress, whatever the cause, according to the stimulus-reflexive theory of Pavlov, *but this defense mechanism is dependent in its intensity and quality on conditioning.* Life as a whole is a struggle against stress induced by environment, its aim a balance between organism and environment by means of adaption.

Therefore we should always examine the behavior of organisms with regard to their entire environment, including past events, and hence infer the underlying design, which furnishes us with all necessary information. However, the strange fact of an actually existing, far-reaching design, whether apparent or real, controlling the behavior of organisms must have a physical foundation, the discovery of which is of the utmost importance. Whether this foundation is termed "directiveness," "fitness," or "design" does not alter the fact that these terms, serving a methodological systematization, contain no explanation whatsoever of the miraculous phenomena. The question of the origin of this inherent design is the problem to be solved.

The animal reacts upon its environment as if it were familiar with its space-time environment and recognizes it. Its behavior is apparently determined by conditions far re-

---

* In his book *Relativity, the Special and the General Theory* (Methuen & Co., London, pp. 55,56), Einstein writes: "That we have not been accustomed to regard the world in this sense as four-dimensioned continuum is due to the fact that in physics, before the advent of the theory of relativity, time played a different and more independent role, as compared with the space-coordinates. It is for this reason that we have been in the habit of treating time as an independent continuum. As a matter of fact, according to classical mechanics, time is absolute, i.e. it is independent of the position and the condition of motion of the system of coordinates. . . . The four-dimensional mode of consideration of the 'world' is natural on the theory of relativity since according to this theory time is robbed of its independence."

moved in space and time. It behaves exactly as if possessing a "knowledge" of the spatially and temporally remote conditions. Providing for the future, it discloses a foresight that seems unattainable to the most ingenious human intelligence. Whence does the organism obtain this knowledge and of what nature is its physical foundation? These are the questions we attempt to solve. As we intend to adhere to established principles of physics, we are obliged to assume that the spatially and temporally removed heterogeneous system of the environment to which the organism adapts itself is somehow physically present in some form in the organism itself.

2. *The Organic Image*

In considering the behavior of animals in relation to their environment as an entirety, we find a condition similar to that of a mirror. Here, too, we consider the whole reflected space, not only the surface of the mirror, in order to gain a satisfactory impression. Although it is the surface that reproduces the complete picture. In this way we perceive the whole reflected space-content as a three-dimensional object totally disconnected from the mediating two-dimensional surface of the mirror.

The behavior of organisms within their environment is similar, but with the basic difference that still another dimension is involved, insofar as the four-dimensional space-time environment radiates its energy upon the three-dimensional organism, and the energy is reflected back into the environment one way or another. No further evidence is necessary to demonstrate the fact that everything we call environment is open to our knowledge and perception only by reason of subjective processes. By experience we gradually learn to infer the produced excitation from the results; or, in other words, to search for the source of the excitations acting upon our sensory organs and gradually develop a more perfect power of reaction to these environmental energies until finally the adult comes to consider his environment as an objective fact. Physiologists, for instance, have produced evidence to support the view that what we see is not an exact reproduction of actuality but an assumption based on past experience.

The analogy to a mirror leads to the idea that an energetic field of the environment is projected into the organism through its surface, thus causing in its interior a real reflection of the environment. Such a reflection of the environment by the sensitive matter of the organism possibly could be the source of all the reaction complexes and functions that would thus appear as "reflected," and the results of which would adapt themselves automatically to the environment. By virtue of such a "reflex activity" in which not only the space but also the time elements of the environment are recorded and then reproduced, it should be possible to reveal the complicated interaction between the interior and the exterior with its momentous consequences culminating in the actual behavior of all animated structures.

To all appearances, the effect produced by the rather intelligent behavior of organisms is as if the system of external forces and tensions is reproduced by the organism; as if an exact plan of the entire environment, true to nature, were part of the organism and, in the manner of a directive center, controlled its actions. For only if the system of the external world is actually inherent in the organism, being as it were projected into it, are its reaction to this system, its adaptability to it, and its most ingenious control of it, comprehensible. Its behavior is obviously not a groping in the dark, a passive being-tossed-about-like-a-ball, nor yet a purely reflex response to accidental excitation; it betrays, rather, properties of a physical order, organization, and system as well as a gradation of the forces governing the environment within a more or less extensive radius, and just this gives rise to the assumption of an equivalent reconstruction existing in the organism.

If we speak here of the very complex external space-time field which is possibly reproduced by organisms, we naturally do not mean an exact replica of the same material as the original. It would be absurd to suppose, to illustrate our meaning by a crude example, that a person admiring a noble edifice and, by allowing it to "impress" itself upon his mind, thus absorbing it mentally, has, in consequence, a miniature-model reproduction of the same material, say concrete, forming in his interior, which may be detected in his anatomy and even removed by a surgical operation. We mean an altogether different kind of reproduction.

Reproductions may be of many kinds. A painting, a photograph, and a silhouette are pictures or reproductions in the narrow sense of the word. A globe, a sculpture, a relief, and the like are also reproductions of physical objects. There need be no conformity between original and reproduction in respect of substance. An engineer's design of an engine to be constructed or a technical installation to be built is also a reproduction. If the reproduction possesses smaller dimensions than its original, we speak of a projection. Great as the material and dimensional difference between design and completed work may be, both may yet contain the same systematic order manifesting itself in the fact that a construction based on a perfect design is unmistakably fixed, so that any able engineer in possession of the plan may erect it in the same manner.

How little dimension actually means becomes evident by the fact that a cube can be represented on a sheet of paper in such a way as to exhibit all necessary dimensions. Similarly, a book describing a foreign country represents a more or less true image of the external reality, if not to the extent of being a model. This is likewise true of a timetable, a directory, a dictionary, and a table of logarithms. He who knows how to read such a book, that is to say, to "assimilate" the drafted system or method, experiences a reproduction of the object described. It seems obvious also to think of a gramophone record, a sound-film, or a piece of music in this connection. Although in these cases there is certainly not the slightest substantial resemblance to the original, we may nevertheless speak of a reproduction insofar as it is possible to reproduce the melody in its original form. Just as the score of a piece of music, consisting of a musical system only, is able to represent a melody, so may the "melody" of the environment be recorded and stored within the organism, ready to be re-created in its original shape. Most interesting perhaps in this respect is the conformity of reproduction to the functional theory. This, at first sight, totally disowns all relationship to its original, and yet it is precisely here that a system is reproduced strictly methodically, capable of being regenerated at any time.

We have to admit that the idea of living organic matter harboring a reproduction of its environment is not novel and has, to some extent, been advanced before. The author believes, however, that there is not merely a limited image of the environment lodged on the retina or in the brain, but that *the entire organic structure constitutes an image. Organism and image are space-temporally equivalent with regard even to their confines.* The reproduction of the environment by the organism probably consists of an equivalent reproduction of essential physical factors, primarily and presumably of physical forces and tensions. That which is reproduced is the complex system of certain energies or of physical manifestations, which, like temperature, entropy, energy, and tension, may be of a gradational, vectorial, or tensional nature. The organic reproduction or image may not only be conceived, it may, contrary to other concepts of biology, also be represented and perceived, since its activity extends into time and space.

The concept of the organic image has been arrived at by inductive reasoning, proceeding from which the deductive inference of theoretical biology should be possible. Contrary to our predecessors, we will, in particular, found the explanation of organic directiveness and of fitness on the concept of an organic image. In the following pages we shall frequently make use of the term "organic image" in place of "organism," in order to stress the faculty of reproducing the environment.

3. *Properties of the Organic Image*

We contend that the whole external space-time system is, somehow, reproduced by organisms in such a way that an unquestionable affinity and coordination is established with regard to the external physical factors. Similar qualities must again appear similar, gradations must correspond to gradations of some kind, instabilities or variabilities must remain instabilities or variabilites, and any anomaly must be rendered as such. The ever-constant factor in all transformations is the organization, grouping, or arrangement of the elements. However dissimilar the organism to its environment, the organism has a physical substratum with an organization and structure, thus constituting an energetic or physical reality.

The difference between the actual organic image and a constructional drawing or a technical reproduction is made obvious by the fact that the living organism is not merely a passive stereotype copy, but a self-maintaining and self-evolving system. Contrary to inanimate products, the living organism actively accomplishes not only the "taking" of the environment, but also its reproduction and preservation. The organism all-powerfully guides or controls the "taking" of the environment and even tries to alter the environment for purposes of its own. We know that a human being is apt to acknowledge and to understand only what he wishes to acknowledge and to understand. He is, to a certain extent, well able to shut his eyes to his surroundings.

In speaking of the environment of an organism, we want to stress again that we do not mean merely the spatial surroundings occupied by the organism. We are thinking more comprehensively of the four-dimensional or space-time section of the universe encompassing it. Quite contrary to a mirror, which is capable of reproducing only the three-dimensional present, we have to deal with four coordinates. An organism also reproduces the past which in turn is reflected back into the present and the future. If we confront the organism with its environment, it occupies only the limited three-dimensional space of the present time, to which, perhaps, may still belong a differential of time; whereas the entire environment comprehends the entire past and future in addition to the greater part of the present. Thus the organism's past and future are regarded as part of its environment, especially its genealogy, or history of origin, the system of which may be reproduced in the present organism. We hold that the traces imprinted in the organism by the environment combine in such a way as to reproduce the system of the environment from which they have arisen. If we conceive the environment in this light, we can also comprehend the existence of a reproduction of genealogy, which no doubt exists, and the physical substratum of which we may find in chromosomes and genes.

The environment could only be reproduced by organisms exactly and completely in the case of unattainable perfection. In reality, that reproduction is always deficient. This deficiency of the organic image may be of a threefold nature: incompleteness, faultiness, and inconsistency.

As to the incompleteness of the organic image, our statement has already made allowance for this. For an image is always more or less biased, and its accuracy is of varying degree, which is well known to us from our knowledge of applied technics. A painting does not reproduce the whole of actual reality; it shows only a certain section of the external color scheme distributed on a plane. A photograph merely renders different shades of light, a silhouette only an outline, and a diagram or a caricature nothing but a few strokes. The fact that the entire environment is never reproduced — merely sections of it, at best — makes the realization of an ideal image impossible. The actual world is so abundant that we could not see, hear, and feel anything at all were we to see, hear, and feel everything. It is at the same time deficient with regard to depth; that is to say, it is incomplete in the reproduction of the submicroscopic world.

To most people, nothing of the world of the infinitesimal is reproduced, much less anything of the elementary particles of matter, or that part of chemistry and physics which deals with atoms and their nuclei, about which research is constantly striving to present a more perfect picture to us. The incompleteness of the image is made especially evident by the fact that it actually shows so little of the past or the future. In any case, fragments only are reproduced, the reproduction of the external world thus remaining imperfect.

Not only does the organic image represent nothing but a section of the environment reproduced, it may also be faulty or erroneous. Images may be dim, pale, indistinct, obliterated, vague, distorted — compare a map or the reflection in a concave or convex mirror — misrepresented, oblique, confused, or altogether incorrect. The following example may serve as an illustration of the manifold possibilities of faultiness in a reproduction. The voice of a singer being unique, it may be reproduced by a gramophone record, but hardly by written or printed notes. Although the record represents a more perfect reproduction, it may yet become faint and indistinct through wear. Incorrect organic images are evoked by delusions, wrong reports, dreams, mistakes, complexes, fixed ideas, and so forth.

And now to the last point — inconsistency. We must bear in mind that the organic image is supposed to be a physical structure represented by the individual organism, with spatial dimensions. Thus it is understandable that there may exist every conceivable gradation or transition between completely separate images and their fusion into an ideal entity. We may, perhaps, designate this condition as disharmony which is well known to our consciousness. The actual image is merely a torso of the desired ideal, and only a modified torso, at that. Nevertheless, the ideal abstraction of a perfect image as reproduced by living matter is the foundation of our argument. In deploring the deficiency of the organic image, we may have primarily thought of ourselves, which is perhaps the most complete and perfect image nature has been able to present so far. If we find fault with this most complete and perfect reproduction to such a degree, it is easy to imagine how much more mediocre the reproduction will be in more primitive creatures, such as lower animals, plants, bacteria, and the like.

From these remarks, perhaps one may be inclined to conclude that the organic image does not greatly differ from a technical reproduction, so that ultimately, with the progress of technology, the artificial production of an organic image or a living structure should also be possible. To suppose this, however, would be quite erroneous. The decisive difference between the two consists in the fact that the organic image is an active, autonomous, or self-maintaining system, operating according to a very complex feedback system, which to a great extent guides or controls the taking of external impressions. We ourselves are best able to observe both factors in the brain. Every moment offers new external impressions (perception, sensations) and inner changes or transformations (judgment, conclusions) without the old ones, i.e. memories, being extinguished. Therefore it is only natural to assume the existence of a strata system of image elements in our brain, layers corresponding to their chronological sequence of acquisition, similar to the manner in which the tectonic strata of the earth's crust reflect its history.

A similar transformation from within must be especially assumed with regard to the so-called "germ track."* Chromosomes and genes build up the organism according to a predetermined design, the basic pattern of which must be firmly established from the very beginning. Mutations may, of course, change this basic pattern in the manner that structural changes affect recurrent changes or self-maintaining systems, to use the terminology of Part One. Mutations furnish opportunities for natural selection as we have suggested in Chapter II, 4. The actualization of the inherited pattern by the living organism certainly is powerfully subjected to external influences, as manifested, for instance, in the regeneration of limbs, tissues, and organs and above all in the normal differentiation within the whole complex system of cells. *Without protracted environmental influences, all cells possibly would have to develop on similar lines, and a differentiation of the cells would be difficult to imagine.* The fact that a cell develops into either a stomach, a nerve,

---

* Germ track: the continuity of sex or germ cells throughout innumerable generations.

or an eye cell could be the result of external influences, including the position of the cell in relation to the other cells of the organism concerned. Almost every signal-pattern received by the brain from the environment opens up new channels there and builds new permanent patterns.

Expressed in terms of psychology, we may say that every cell possibly possesses a uniform fundamental knowledge on which is superimposed a special knowledge that is a function of the condition of the whole. This may be clearly observed in human society, which in this respect is truly comparable to an organism composed of a great number of individual cells.

4. *Evidence of the Organic Image*

We have deduced by reasoning the concept of an organic image from the functional position of the organism within its entire environment. But how does this idea agree with practical experience? Does the structure and function, the anatomy, morphology, histology, or physiology of organisms confirm the view put forward in the preceding chapters?

With regard to the physical substratum of the organic image, which cannot possibly be lacking, it is not easy to get any direct confirmation of our concept by observation, as the reproduction must necessarily be of a totally different nature from the original, which is represented by the space-time environment. We once more remind the reader of a gramophone record, which, to judge by outward appearances, possesses no material similarity whatsoever to its original, which consists mostly of melodiously combined sound waves. However, it might be possible to grasp the engraved system of harmony by a sufficient magnification of the furrows with their overlapping oscillations, waves, and vibrations. Musically trained people are able to recognize the scheme of a melody from a sheet of music and to experience it, or, rather, hear it, with their mind's ear only. It is considerably more difficult to recognize the existing reproduction on an undeveloped film. And, last but not least, who would be able to infer the respective originals from a Chinese script, or even a treatise on functional theory, if he were not acquainted with the symbols in the former or the specific terminology in the latter? So our task seems a sheer impossibility with regard to organic life, where the reproduction may reach far down into the world of the minute and infinitesimal, completely inaccessible to us. And yet the discovery of the energetic system reproduced by organisms does not seem at all hopeless.

The nucleus of a cell represents an organic image of the surrounding medium, which is the cytoplasm. It is rather difficult to conceive of effective nuclear control of the complex cytoplasmic processes without the transfer of information from the cytoplasm to the nucleus and in the reverse direction. A feedback principle seems to be involved here, supporting the concept of the organic image. If, for instance, we ask how the chromosomes come to align themselves in the correct geometric pattern before they separate in mitosis, and how sister chromosomes find their way to opposite poles, we realize that we are faced with an order of problems that does not fit into current methods of thinking about biological events. The concept of the organic image seems to be the only possible way in which a solution to this problem may be arrived at. In this connection we should bear in mind the similarity of configurative effects to the orientating effect of electromagnetic fields of force upon structurally nonisotropic particles.

To the organic reproductive power, furthermore, belong projection and transmission apparatus, organs, fibrils, and the like, which form the necessary connection between the organic image and its environment. Anyone looking for this will at once think of the eye, which provides an excellent example with which to confirm our statements. The eye, like a photographic camera, with lens, vitreous humor, diaphragm, retina, and the rest, projects into the interior a reproduction, true to nature, of the external picture. Here nature has created a specific organ of reproduction with the technical details of whose optical functioning we are well acquainted.

Just as a picture is taken with the camera so that the subject is reproduced on the film, the eye receives the external picture on the retina, which then, by means of the optic nerve, transmits that picture into the interior. The part of the retina upon which the lens focuses the image of the object we see is only a tiny speck. This minute patch is then enlarged about a thousand times and projected on the visual area of the brain, just as a picture is transmitted by television. The similarity between the eye, consisting of organic matter, and television, containing glass and metal, is striking indeed. The idea of an actual organic image having first arisen as a vision originating in the technical analogy of the mirror loses its somewhat hypothetical character by referring it to the human eye, whereby it receives a material foundation. A more striking piece of evidence can hardly be conceived. We have reason to assume that the brain is the seat of a central picture or image, although we shall hardly succeed in proving the reproduction of the environmental system here as easily as it is possible on the retina.

The eye is undoubtedly that organic structure which furnishes us with the best material evidence for the concept of organic images, but certainly not the only one. Otherwise, how would the systematic behavior of eyeless organisms, or, for that matter, of any separate organs, be explainable? To trace all life simply to the existence of images and their corresponding projection apparatus would compel us, in order to establish convincing proof, to examine the entire organic world with this end in view. And we could doubtless do this successfully. Take, for instance, the ear. This, too, is an organ of projection, primarily transmitting the temporal sequence of sounds, the melody of the vibrations of the air. But the nose, the tongue, the skin, and so on, also project sections or parts of the environment into the interior, although, perhaps, less perfectly and of a less differentiated order.

The image projected into the somatic sensory-projection area in the brain, i.e. the region where sensations of touch are received from all parts of our body, is that of a somewhat distorted miniature of ourselves. These distortions are related to the more important patterns of our everyday lives, making certain organs or limbs more important than others. Further down the scale of evolution, these distortions become less and less obvious in agreement with the less involved action and reaction patterns of more primitive organisms. Modern techniques of observing and interpreting electro-encephalograms should furnish us with sufficient evidence in order to prove that the brain and nervous system are the seat of a central image reproducing the present environmental system as interpreted by the sense organs.

Proceeding from nature's unique masterpieces, the eye and the brain, passing on to the structure and method of functioning of other sensory organs, and lastly following up the further transmission by means of nerves, it is possible to prove with empirical exactness the correctness of our assumption for a wide province of life. Taking in the same way the basic facts of the eye and the brain as a starting point, and proceeding gradually to the psychology of the other sensory organs, the concept of the organic image may be put to the test in every sphere of life and be made the object of experimental research. Our statement that organic matter exhibits a universal receptive faculty for reproductions of the environment and that, in a certain sense, all organic matter possesses eyes, ears, brain and receptive sensory organs, is nothing but a generalization of the functioning of the eye.

The phenomenon called "heredity" presupposes a reproduction of the past by the present individual being. Heredity may also be considered as the physiological counterpart of another phenomenon, which psychology terms "memory." To remember is to experience events we recall, and to imitate. Everything we do, every thought and action, depends upon the ability to repeat experiences. And, in fact, the properties of memory are quite frequently, if not everywhere, to be met in the organic. In humans it is obviously most perfectly manifested in the brain and nervous system. The psychology of animals teaches us how marked is their development in this respect. And descending in the history of animal evolution, no considerable qualitative change justifies the supposition of an insurmountable boundary. A certain kind of memory system assuredly exists in the chromosomes and genes, which explains the repeated creation of the same type. This also includes the reproduction of biological structures and molecules, as well as the organization of multicellular matter in organisms. Experts on the subject even speak of memory as a general function of all life, which accords with our view. We are fully justified in including in the concept of memory all involuntary reproductions of sensations, imaginings, emotions, dispositions, and inclinations, thus accepting *memory by itself as a possible primary faculty or power of life, the source and unifying bond of all conscious life.*

Having so far dealt mostly with the relation between the environment and the organism proceeding from it, we now have to discuss the relationship in the reverse direction, for the process of reproduction should to a certain extent be reversible too. The gray matter of the brain, for instance, is a generator of electrical impulses, and the messages the brain receives from the environment by the sense organs are likewise electrical. Just as the external event is transmitted into the cellular structure by means of the sensory organs, by members or limbs, such as feelers, antennae, tentacles, eyestalks, or hair, through the centripetal, sensatorial or afferent nerves to the brain, so is the internal event occurring in the organism projected into the outer world by means of the centrifugal, efferent or motor nerves, by glands, muscles, arms, legs, tentacles, parapodia, pseudopodia, flagella, cilia, fins, wings, stinging hairs, teeth, tails, nippers or pincers, lashes, claws, stings, horns and antlers, as well as tools and weapons.

An excellent illustration of this is provided by the existence of a similar projection or transmission apparatus, corresponding to the receptive apparatus. Striking examples are the sensory areas of the brain, if compared to the motor areas. Microscopic investigation reveals, for instance, that the strata arrangement of cells is reversed. The centrifugal and centripetal nerves have already been mentioned as counterparts scarcely distinguishable from each other in appearance. However, the eye, too, possesses its opposite in nature. There are fish whose luminous organs — monocentris japonicus, anomalops, photoblepharon, and so on — are reflectorlike, and inhabitants of the deep sea — sepiola ligulata — that even possess lenses focusing light waves and refracting light in an outward direction. Often enough it is only the function of a differently constructed organ that represents an opposite. Thus the function of the ear is the reversed function of the mouth, the latter producing the sound waves which the former receives. The interchange between the internal and the external world — between the human organism and the environment — is clearly exemplified in speech and counter-speech. A certain exposition into the external world takes place in gesticulation, that is to say, when an oral description is accompanied by involuntary movements of the hands or by some other gesture.

First and foremost, however, the limbs convey to the exterior the projection of the forces active in the living organism. The limbs alter the position of the organism within the surroundings by locomotion, and form the environment by producing commodities, structures, webs or fabrics, nets, dens or burrows, houses, hives, and nests, in the manner done especially by man on a large scale. The limbs provide food, ward off enemies, and in many ways interfere with the formation and evolution of the environment. In all these cases a reciprocity of taking and projecting between original and organic image is manifested, which, as will be expounded later, makes expedient animal behavior more intelligible to us.

5. The Autonomous and the Induced Somatic Forces of the Organism

The concept of the organic image allows of a quite far-reaching conclusion. If the tensions and stresses of the environmental field is to be reproduced by the organism, the latter should reveal physiological tensions and stresses corresponding to those of the former. This should then induce the organism to adjust its behavior-patterns accordingly. We know today that, to a great extent, the action-reaction pattern of mammals results from inner physiological stress induced by external events. The so-called alarm reaction and the general adaption syndrome bear out this statement. Any kind of stress that surpasses the average or normal level acts on the pituitary gland. This gland replies by mobilizing the adrenals, which in turn discharge the hormones responsible for the reaction pattern of the individual.

It is possible *to trace response in animal behavior to two different causes*: the primary or autonomous somatic forces originating in the organism itself; and the secondary or induced somatic forces released by energy patterns entering the organism from without. The primary somatic forces are produced by the needs of metabolism and by sexual desire in general. It is sufficient to mention only hunger, thirst, pain-avoidance, curiosity, and the emptying of vessels and glands of secretional matter which are identified by the so-called organic sensations. Primary and secondary somatic forces are separated by signal limits only; they are, however, liable to transmission into each other by gradual transformation.

Of course, the conditions are surveyable only as long as primary and secondary somatic forces do not collide. If both forces appear simultaneously, their interrelations and the resulting animal actions are not always discernible. Let us only recall the vectorial summation of forces and the phenomenon of activation. Here follow a few examples showing that secondary forces are the indirect cause of the activation of primary forces. Play and sport, besides the animal instincts, mostly require an additional, external impulse. Induced forces play a certain role in nourishment also. The sight of certain dishes provokes a desire to eat them; *"l'appétit vient en mangeant,"* as the French saying aptly puts it. Crying or weeping is usually caused by external impulses.

The interrelation of primary and secondary somatic forces is particularly striking in sexual activity, whereas in nonsexual generation primary forces exclusively or pre-eminently take effect. However, autonomous and induced somatic forces emanating from a sexual partner combine in bisexual generation. It seems as if the aim of nature to develop in the organism a capacity for resonance of induced somatic forces were the reason for bisexual generation. This happens in every kind of erotic activity with a partner, that is to say, in dancing, flirting, caressing, kissing, and similar contacts. There is everywhere an interrelation of both factors, which is not surprising when it is considered that, according to the parallelogram, two forces or quantities coexisting in space and time will combine, though of different origin or will — at least, not continue side by side without reciprocal influence.

This duality of the activating forces is also expressed by the internal functions of the organism, which results in a characteristic classification of it. The primary somatic forces aim at a direct degradation of energy in connection with metabolism and work performed, while the secondary somatic forces also lead to an increase of energy, assimilation, growth, regeneration, adaptability with regard to circumstances, the formation of communities, mutual assistance, social activities, and so forth. The primary somatic forces should, in general, correspond to egotistic impulses and the secondary somatic forces to altruistic impulses.

The primary and secondary somatic forces and, in addition, the forces resulting from the interaction of both are perhaps one reason why three main organic functions are to be distinguished. They are: metabolic and other autonomous functions, functions induced by passive reception of energetic impressions (or sense impressions) from the environment, and, finally, activity of the organism resulting from the two functions first mentioned. In fact, this functional division leads to a tripartition of organs, and physiologically we may distinguish:

1) metabolic organs like the mouth, gullet, heart, kidneys, stomach, liver, gall bladder, and spleen;
2) organs transmitting the environment to the interior

like the skin, nose, ears, eyes, sensatorial nerves, all
the sensory organs, and the brain; and

3) organs transmitting the final internal event to the
environment like motor nerves, limbs, glands, and
the brain.

Although at every place within the organism primary and
secondary somatic forces should be simultaneously present,
the structure of the organism involves the fact that only one
specific function may be the sole purpose of a special organ.
Thus the purpose of the eye is the optical transmission of
"recordings" into the interior, which does not exclude the
fact that each eye cell possesses a metabolism of its own and
may also be active in some other way.

The tripartition of organs is also to some extent a feature
of plants, though in a less differentiated and perfect degree.
The existence of papillae, excitable organs, and the like bears
witness to the fact that the difference between the animal
kingdom and the plant world is only one of degree and not
of kind. The subdivision of individual plants into roots,
stalks, and leaves, as well as the occasional development of
sensory organs, is indeed a progressive specialization of metabolism and the generative mechanism.

The separation of autonomous and induced somatic forces
must manifest itself also in phylogenetic evolution. Disregarding any environmental influences on organisms like natural
selection, the primary forces or, differently expressed, the
physical correlations of metabolic necessities, of sexual instinct, of instinct for curiosity, play and sport, and of aestheti-
cal necessities are perhaps capable of initiating primary evolution. This could result not only in an increase in size of the
species but also in an increase of progeny, in a relative growth
of individual organs, and in the evolution of natural tendencies in a direction already taken. This could even lead to
an exaggerated development of certain organs, such as horns,
mandibles, and other supergenerations. The aesthetic instinct
could also take an active part in the development of shape
and color.

In so-called *orthogenesis* the evolutionary tendency is without relevance to its environment. Contrary to this, the induced somatic forces may cause adaption of species to the environment, progressive formation of communities, or extensive care for the progeny, and so forth. In any case, two evolutionary tendencies, between which there exists no gradual transition because their respective origins are basically of quite different kinds, become evident.

6. *Activity, Passiveness, and Harmony*

As we find it necessary to repeatedly discuss the active and passive behavior of organisms, organs, cells, etc., we intend to classify these actions according to physical concepts. The distinction will be based on the increase or loss of entropy of a limited space. Although the second law of thermodynamics states that entropy is increased by any event or process whatsoever, if many molecules are involved, it does not say that the increase of entropy must actually occur at a given place. A local loss or decrease of entropy or the creation of negative entropy is possible indeed, provided this loss is supercompensated by a juxtaposed increase of entropy in some other place. On the strength of this, every event may be split up into partial processes so that processes of the one kind exclusively represent an increase of entropy, while those of the other kind constitute a local loss of entropy.

Let us imagine a cylindrically enclosed space filled with an ideal gas and divided into two separate halves by a movable, immaterial piston. In space 1 the pressure equals p^1 and the entropy s^1, corresponding to p^2 and s^2 in space 2. If $p^1 > p^2$ and $s^1 > s^2$, the frictionless piston is being shifted until $p^1 = p^2$ and $s^1 = s^2$. In the same way the whole process of equalization of pressure may be divided into two fictitious partial processes occurring in space 1 and space 2 respectively. By the automatic displacement of the piston, the change of conditions in space 1 is accompanied by an increase of entropy, while that in space 2 incurs a loss of entropy. The decrease of entropy in space 2 is possible because this half of the cyclindrical space does not represent an isolated system in a thermodynamical sense.

Processes occurring in an "open" or nonisolated partial system resulting in an increase of entropy may be called "active," and "passive" when they incur a decrease of entropy. Specific terminology expresses this distinction by saying that the gas in space 1 is expanding, whereas the gas in space 2 is being compressed. Accordingly, it might be said that the gas in space 1 is "active," whereas that in space 2 is "passive" in suffering compression. So then, according to our definition, activity and passiveness are no more identical than are the local increase and decrease of entropy.

Although a change exclusively active may occur within a system, passive processes must be always juxtaposed by active ones. An enclosed gas can expand in certain conditions without affecting any other system, but it is absolutely impossible that gas be compressed without some other system being active in causing the compression. An active event may occur "of itself," while a passive sufferance presupposes some active event occurring outside the system in question.

We conclude that *forces resulting in actions are a characteristic of the inner forces or tendencies of a system, whereas those causing passiveness reflect external forces or influences on a system.* This discrimination between active and passive processes is of great significance for the study of animal behavior, for the difference between internal and external forces, between active "doing" and passive "suffering," always play an important role in the description of vital phenomena.

The changes of an organism may be, as we have explained in Chapter II, 5, the result of either somatic forces, or of external coercion or interference. Mostly, both factors come into play. In the former instance, the processes are more or less functional and self-evolving, such as metabolism, growth, adaptation, regeneration, ageing, and automatic wear and tear; not only the recurring somatic changes, but also an active structural change of the soma from within may be noticed. In the instance of external coercion or interference, we may observe that not only the recurring functions but also the soma is affected and altered. Such interferences are, among others, destruction, killing, violence, rape, injury, wear and tear by external use, narcotization, tormenting; and the object in question suffers active as well as passive structural changes. Frequently, active inner drives may be caused secondarily by external conditions. The active defense of an animal is often called forth by an aggressor in this way. Mostly, external circumstances stimulate a human being to activity.

A condition in which the internal and external tendencies of an organism are in concord may be called "harmony." This harmonious agreement exists between the respiratory process of animals and vegetable growth. Organic life has likewise adjusted itself to the activity of the sun to such a degree that, on the whole, it may be said to harmonize. Other examples of harmony are the interplay between pollinating insects and honey-yielding plants; intercellular co-operation; the interlacement of agricultural, commercial, and industrial functions, and the like. Any kind of symbiosis reveals a harmonious relationship.

We ourselves are in harmony with our environment if we voluntarily and deliberately accept its influence or interference, and do not merely suffer it passively. A marriage, a friendship, an organization, or a working partnership based on these foundations is said to be harmonious. The organization of organisms from their component elements presupposes harmonious relationships. *The nature of normal and healthy organisms is such that harmonious interrelationships exist between the individual and component organs as well as between each of the latter and its basic elements (individual cells) in turn.* Individual cells and organs reproduce the fields created by their environment which is composed again by other cells and organs, according to the concept of organic image. Harmonious relationships pervading the whole organism from basic element to basic element may be termed *"harmonic bonds."**

---

* Harmonic bonds are explainable as mutually stabilizing electrical and chemical functions operating between cells and cell systems. Generally a very slight additional stimulus (electrical or chemical), precisely timed, is required to offset any bond-disrupting tendency to build up.

This "democratic" *principle of simultaneous autonomy and subordination, of self-assertion and association* — perhaps the most important principle for the understanding of life, and valid for every level of organization — accounts for the specific character of all organic events. A picture taken from human society will illustrate this. Here also each "unit" is controlled or guided by its higher "authorities," but without becoming a passive or mechanical tool of the latter. In spite of sub- or co-ordination, there always remains a kind of autonomy revealing an activity and spontaneity of its own with regard to associated "members."

Deprived of "harmonic bonds," that is to say, without the complementary function of cells, tissues, organs, an organism breaks up into its component parts, which has an important bearing on the life-span of the individual itself, since the organization of the elements has lost its *raison d'être,* its reason for existence. But not so a machine, the working functions of which are not subservient to its component elements. A machine may stand still without injury to itself. Yet if the harmonic activity of an organism ceases, the connection between the basic elements is dissolved, as they no longer have any interest in the union. Therefore an organism can never be without harmonic bonds, and metabolism must incessantly continue, be it even in so minute a degree as occurs in so-called suspended animation.

Chapter III

PSYCHOLOGICAL ASPECTS OF THE ORGANIC IMAGE

1. *The Natural Sciences and Psychology*

We have now arrived at a stage in our argumentation at which the use of psychological terminology becomes appropriate in the description of the organic mechanism of reproduction, particularly when referring to the brain.

In everyday life as well as in science, in practical application as well as in theory, we customarily make a distinction between two spheres that differ in nature and fundamental phenomena. These are the sphere of physical, bodily, or material phenomena, on the one hand, and the sphere of psychological, mental, or intellectual experience, on the other. The hackneyed phrase "body and soul"— consciousness, spirit, mind — presents this idea in a nutshell. We sometimes speak also of the "external world" in contrast to the "inner or internal world," expressing the same distinction.

Physical phenomena are light, color, sound, a stone, a cloud, a plant, man, motion, atoms, energy, and so on. Psychological experiences are the sensation of color, imagination, an impulse or instinct, pain, happiness, thought, pride, enthusiasm. The difference is clear to anybody, and there is hardly ever any difficulty as to the classification of such phenomena. The term "natural phenomena" is in general applied to phenomena the correlations of which are the subject of natural sciences, whereas the term "experiences" denotes all phenomena the reciprocal relationships of which are the study of psychology. Logic and the theory of cognition may be regarded as subdivisions of this science, as they try to establish certain rules and laws with regard to the interrelations and interdependencies of cognitions and conceptions, of mental experiences.

Before examining the justification for such a sharp division as is customary and also maintained by us, before inquiring into what unites or separates the two realms and before establishing an infallible characteristic for either in the nature of a definition, we first compare psychological with physical phenomena and vice versa as the subjects of various sciences. This will furnish us with a purely practical means of recognizing at once to which of the two realms each separate phenomenon belongs, should for some reason or other such classification prove necessary. Of the two, the natural sciences, to some extent including biology, are founded on a comparatively sound basis, and in spite of the vast domain of specialized research there are but few differences of opinion, which are soon eliminated by the rapid development of the natural sciences. There is no doubt as to their respective aims and the way to attain them.

Not quite so in psychology. Nevertheless, we have to deal with a definite science; and some subdivisions, such as logic and the theory of cognition, seem to be firmly grounded. The methods of the mental sciences including psychoanalysis are, however, not very firmly grounded. The reason why the mental sciences are at a disadvantage as compared with the natural sciences is to be found in the fact that scientific psychology is to a large extent dependent on collaboration with the natural sciences.

Our whole physical universe and all the natural phenomena are of our perceptions and cognitions, which becomes especially evident from the fact that we generally define them as the "contents" of cognitions. Every natural phenomenon is either directly or indirectly felt, perceived, recognized, approached, and so on. It is the *content* of the cognition, this word being understood in its widest possible sense, and, in particular, the *object* of sensations, perceptions, emotions, observations, imaginations, realizations, opinions, conclusions, and the like. Never and nowhere does any natural phenomenon exist for us, unless it be part of experience, viz. a cognition. Every physical phenomenon becomes indirectly associated with psychological phenomena, with impulses, sensations, and so on, only by first entering upon the cognition.

Thus our cognitions are necessarily accompanied by impulses, emotions, actions, and so forth. In addition, they possess a content in the form of physical phenomena, such as forces, energy, work performed, and so on. Now the question is: What relations exist between the accompanying experiences, on the one hand, and the contents of cognitions, on the other, both of which are somehow connected through the medium of the cognitions? Following up these connections, we will obtain correlations linking external physical phenomena and inner experiences, a procedure which we intend to adopt.

2. *Empirical Relations Linking Impulses and Forces*

Mechanics supplies us with the experiencing of the physical relaxation of a tense spring. The recognition of a possible relaxation of a tense spring may easily evoke the desire to witness that relaxation. There are also strong inducements to release the mechanical tensions of toys. This impulse or "drive" is primarily aimed at the ultimate end, viz. the experience of relaxation, but also at every intermediate stage that is likely to further the attainment of the final aim.

Conditions are much the same in the release of gas compressed in an oxygen cylinder. Here the desire is aroused to witness the escape of the gas. The connection between the sight of a tautly inflated balloon and the impulse to prick it with a pin, or burst it with a burning cigarette, is perhaps especially credible. Analogous conceptions of possible events inspire the desire to experience or witness the bursting of a dam, the fall of a loosened rock, or of a raised steam hammer, a landslide, the collapse of a huge building, and so on; to have the certainty of these events coming to pass or to know at least that steps have been taken to precipitate them. Some further examples taken from physics are the psychological tension and relaxation evoked by a large waterfall, by electrical discharges like lightning, short circuits, and by relaxations of tension after a thunderstorm.

Chemistry furnishes still more examples. The depreciation or dissipation of energy during combustion, which is equivalent to relaxation or entropy increase, has a marked psychological effect. A fire alarm excites our imagination and we are seized by the desire personally to witness the raging fire. Everybody hurries to the scene of the conflagration and, succumbing to the spell of the awe-inspiring spectacle, is lost to the rest of the world. The visualization of an explosion, evoked by the sight of a burning fuse leading to a powder barrel, creates the desire to witness or to avoid the event. As long as we ourselves are in safety and need not fear any consequences detrimental to our own interests, only exceedingly strong counter-impulses will normally induce us to leave the scene before the realization of our desire. The sight of a loaded weapon makes us visualize its discharge, thus evoking the wish to hear the shot. A torchlight procession is a very effective, and therefore an attractive and desirable, spectacle. Similar phenomena exciting strong desires and impulses are the flaring of a match, spectacular chemical processes, such as fireworks, bombs, rocket, volcanic eruptions, and the like. The success of movies, theaters, shows, circuses, and races of all kinds are mostly based on these psychophysical correlations.

In biology, we like to experience the relaxation of physical or physiological tensions. Consider the spectacular feeding of beasts at a zoo. The starvation and suffering of our fellow beings inspires us with a desire to mitigate their condition, to join charitable enterprises, and similar activites.

The connecton or interrelation demonstrated above is really best observable in one's own mind. The sight of food arouses either appetite or aversion. The sensation of highly charged glands provokes the desire to feel their relaxation by secretion. The imagined possibility of sexual relaxation or satisfaction above all acts as an incentive to sexual desire. The thought of a possible release of tension or stress calls forth a corresponding need for discharge. Boils, tumors, ulcers, pimples, and the like are centers of tension and excess pressure. They create an impulse to squeeze or cut them open. The idea of possible relaxation after fatigue and exhaustion evokes a desire for sleep and rest. The knowledge of a possible compensation of temperatures during excessive cold or heat inspires us with the wish for moderate temperatures. The feeling of some impediment, especially in respect of movement, creates a fierce longing for freedom. Being fettered, we wish to burst our shackles.

Although a longing exists to eliminate and equalize tensions or stress, this feeling is entirely absent when tensions are to be created. Aversion is, on the contrary, the common feeling in many cases of the kind. If tensions are nevertheless created, they are mostly nothing but a means to an end, serving the attainment of some other aim, usually that of a later relaxation. We cock the trigger of a popgun, but only to make the gun explode. We pull a toboggan uphill in order to coast down.

But it is not always the discrete distinctive acts, the changes of structure or shape spoken of so far, that are of paramount desirability. To an even greater extent do we desire to experience another group of phenomena, that is, permanent transformations of energy and the resulting depreciation or degradation of energy, which is equivalent to continuous physical relaxation. Such permanent phenomena may be stationary or steady as, for instance, the flowing of a river. We feel pleasure at the sight of fountains, cataracts, and creeping glaciers, the monotonous progress of which ensures a continuous transformation of energy.

Frequently permanent events consist of a chain of cyclic processes similar to those already discussed under the heading of recurrent change in Part One. For this reason we enjoy spinning a top, rolling a hoop, or manipulating any kind of mechanical toy that rotates or performs cyclic movements. The rhythmical sequence of cyclic processes is the best guarantee for the uninterrupted continuance of an event, and its transformation and degradation of energy.

We like to observe such a continuous rhythm, preferably when it involves our own body. That is why we dance and swing or rock, go on the merry-go-round and the roller coaster, or perform rhythmic movements at games and sports. Even the hardest labor is made easier by the spell of rhythm. A permanent degradation of energy is insured not only by rhythmical movements, but also by nonrhythmical functions of organisms. That is the reason for our enjoyment of the playing and romping of children and animals; we keep dogs or birds, cultivate plants or aquariums, and the like. Our love of nature is also inspired by this same instinct.

And lastly, there is yet another group of phenomena we aspire to. These are phenomena expressive of harmony, while we reject those representing disharmony. We are fond of a work of art and a melody because of their harmoniousness. We aspire to a harmonious marriage, a harmonious friendship, a harmonious social life and, last but not least, a harmoniously balanced character. This is self-evident if we consider that a state devoid of tension is defined as harmony, and disharmony as a state replete with tensions and stress.

Most impulses are not directed at the final aim, however, but rather at the attainment of the intermediate stages. Such, for instance, is the striving after property, fortune, money, power, and the like, which may be attained by devious stages. Analogously, most actions are only a means to an end. The poet says: Unless philosophy keeps the world on the move, this world will be governed by hunger and love. This is, of course, correct only if the definitions of hunger and love are taken in a very wide sense. To hunger and love we would at least add curiosity and the instinct for play and sport. For the attraction exercised upon us by manipulation, play, and sport might easily persuade us to regard them as ends in themselves.

3. *The Law of Motive Power and Consequences*

A.) Much more might be said about the few experiments just cited. But enough has been indicated to establish a basis for the deduction of the law of motive power:

The perception of a possible relaxation of a physical stress or tension induces a drive (impulse) tending toward experiencing the relaxation of that stress or tension.

Whereas the aim of the tension is physical, the aim of the drive is psychological. The two seem to be otherwise identical. To be precise, their relation is as follows: the psychological aim is the experience of a cognition; the physical aim is the content of that same cognition. Thus the two aims agree to the utmost extent of agreement possible for psychological and physical phenomena. The fundamental law formulated above affords a vast field of research for both experimental physiological psychology and psychosomatic medicine.

To prove the validity of our empirical law it is necessary to select such phenomena as are not too closely accompanied by additional disturbing factors and conceptions. The relation to be proved will become manifest only if the experiment deals with rather isolated and well-defined phenomena for observation. When experimenting, the undivided attention of the observer must be riveted upon one single and definite phenomenon, leaving him indifferent to everything else capable of confusing him. A successful and incontestable proof depends upon the strict observance of this precaution.

This law of motive power is empirical, a fact which may be verified by experiments, as has been suggested by several examples. In spite of this, proofs are not so easily established, since a single, well-defined physical condition rarely presents itself to our cognition. Usually the existing phenomena perceived by a person are already so highly complex as to exclude unobjectionable conditions for an experiment. The more so as, besides the accompanying phenomena, many subsequent results of the phenomena are simultaneously recognized. Hence, the perception of a physical phenomenon generally arouses a number of simultaneous impulses of differing tendency and intensity, which may even be directed against each other. The result is a bewildering multiplicity of impulses, drives, tensions, capable of effacing the real connection, which consequently is not clear discernible among the abundance of cognitions assailing the observer.

To give an example: the spectacle of a great fire, whatever attraction it may exercise upon us, will in most spectators evoke the realization of the destruction of valuable property, and perhaps even the realization of danger to life. The desire to witness the fire is then overwhelmed by the far stronger impulse to rescue endangered lives and property. Instead of adding to the fire, everybody does his utmost to extinguish it, in spite of its otherwise powerful attraction. Often enough, as already pointed out, the results of a phenomenon determine the release of an impulse, the conditions thus becoming very complicated and involved.

It is not always easy to recognize what constitutes the potent physical relaxation or degradation of energy in the visualized phenomena actuating mental impulses. Such include festive occasions, celebrations, processions, entertainments, meetings, shows, ceremonies, exhibitions, theatrical performances, and so on. These events are mostly not associated with actual physical relaxation or energy dissipation the spectator could be interested in; they merely arouse the illusion of a possible relaxation, which suffices for the release of psychic impulses. Parties and festivities are a welcome occasion for picking up new acquaintances, while dancing may involve sexual sensations. To create an illusion is often enough the sole object of theatrical performances and novels. And as often as not we sober down when we realize that we have not drawn nearer our ultimate aim after all.

According to the law of motive power, mental impulses tend toward a possible relaxation of tension that is equivalent to degradation of energy. In other words, impulses not only are aimed at a direct increase of entropy, but also at an indirect increase of entropy. A long detour is often the surest way to the attainment of the final objective. Released impulses may also break down into separate components, each of which will be always directed toward the attainment of an intermediate stage leading indirectly to the ultimate aim. Thus mental impulses are not, so to speak, directed only toward the growing of the corn and the ripening of the fruit, but also toward sowing and tillage, processes conducive to and promoting a probable later enjoyment of the fruit. Not only do we want to see an inflated balloon burst, we want to see the approach of the pin which is to cause its bursting.

Riding on a roller coaster, we take greater pleasure in the downward glide, which involves an equalization of tensions. Yet the uphill ride is not devoid of pleasurable anticipation, as this alone renders the subsequent plunge possible. Not only do we wish to dwell comfortably, we are even willing to have a house built, should there be no other choice. The desire to witness some interesting spectacle includes also the wish to go there. Anything preceding and furthering the realization of a phenomenon striven for is desirable too.

The law of motive power contains the statement that the aim of an impulse is identical with the physical aim of a perceived or recognized possibility of relaxation. Let us illustrate this by a few examples. The impulse to see a spring released is in accord with the tension of the spring. The desire to witness the bursting of an inflated balloon operates parallel to the forces of the gas pressure. At the sight of a fire, fireworks, an explosion, and so forth, the mental impulses are directed toward the perception of the same phenomena as those which are the aim of the actually active forces of combustion. The sight of a waterfall, the slide down a toboggan run, sexual or any other kind of physical activity — all are governed by the same psychophysical correlation.

Whereas impulses tend toward the experiencing of a cognition, the forces themselves tend toward a physical aim representing the content of that cognition. Their distinction lies in the fact that they belong to two different spheres; they are, however, directed at the same aim. To put it still differently: the relation between released mental impulses and releasing cognitions is the same as that between the physical forces and the corresponding contents of cognitions. The source of the mental impulses is a certain cognition, their aim is another definite cognition. *Physical forces running parallel to the mental impulses govern the corresponding contents of cognition.*

The indirect aims should, in fact, be distinguished from the direct aims. The sight of jewelry, fine clothes, motor cars, a country house, and, last but not least, money, creates covetousness, that is, the desire or mental impulse to possess these things. Their possesion will, then, be a step nearer to the main objective, namely, their utilization. We take great pains to avoid the possibly disastrous consequences of a fire, preventing therefore a possible "relaxation." We do not avail ourselves of the direct pleasure of eating all the food produced but curb our immediate appetite by keeping part of the crop to plant for a future harvest. Everything impeding our progress toward the realization of our aim is removed. The difference separating the aim proper and the intermediate stages is the same as that which exists between "an end" and the "means to an end."

Special attention should be paid to the distinction between physical phenomena and experiences, as they become apparent here. For while our indirect aims may, in their physical aspect, consist in an accumulation of free energy, which is synonymous to material wealth, their mental aspect will always represent a later utilization and dissipation, i.e. relaxation, satisfaction. This is explainable by the fact that we create a tension only if we are convinced that by doing so we will promote a future relief of tension. If we earn our money at great effort or under hard conditions, and in this way accumulate "free" or "available" energy, the knowledge of the manifold future relaxations we shall enjoy spending it fills us with gratification. This fact remains even if the calculation should subsequently prove erroneous.

If, in fact, the various forms of energy entering the human organism are co-ordinated to cognitions, we may say that the whole organism feels or perceives its environment. This psychological or mental image, arising from cognition, in the widest sense of the word, is identical with knowledge.

Quantity and quality of reception depend, among other things, upon attention, presence of mind, and the perceptive faculties of the individual. Many cognitions are achieved by mental effort, such as paying attention, thinking, reflection, considering, judging, and so on. Impulses and drives really seem to be equivalent to physical forces and tensions.*

B.) The system of the environment reproduced by the organism actually seems to be the same in the sphere of physical phenomena as in the world of psychological phenomena. Therefore, we may also say that our knowledge depicts our four-dimensional or space-time environment in the present all at once. *Just as the living organism reproduces the space-time environment — hence also including the past — memory, which is the psychological counterpart of the organic image, reproduces past and present experiences simultaneously.*

In the same manner as we intend to prove that the organic image is a basic concept of all life, so is memory its corresponding psychical counterpart. Every new perception creates new "structural changes" in the "self-maintaining" substratum of the brain. Here the importance of the mental element becomes evident. Not being able to survey completely the physical phenomena as well as the psychological phenomena with our limited intellectual powers, we gain a more perfect picture if we take both aspects into consideration. For it is indeed possible to complement our imperfect knowledge of the one sphere by our knowledge of the other.

Knowledge of the past implies a simultaneous knowledge of future events. This is true insofar as the events are not subject to chance. In general, the prediction of an event is nothing but a transposition of the past into the future, in accordance with experience and logic. The statements made earlier with regard to the imperfection of the organic image also may be applied to the imperfection of knowledge. Our supposed knowledge may be incomplete, inconsistent, and incorrect, a fact we try to remedy by constant increase and readjustment of it.

---

* These problems are discussed more fully in the Appendix.

The mental aspect of the organic image may be identified with the "subjective" element or the "I," whose opposite is the original of the image or environment and identical with the "objective" element or the "you." The psychological view indicated here may be considerably extended and is most conspicuous in man, where the conditions are more familiar to us and the mental experiences directly accessible. On the strength of our exposition, the concept of the organic image seems no longer strange to us, for in the mental sphere we strive quite consciously to attain as truthful an image of the entire environment as possible.

In fact, it is extraordinary to think that the reproduction of the environment should once more be reproduced, and more deeply inward at that. Nevertheless, man is able to perceive the origin of his knowledge, and the relations or connections between separate cognitions by introspection; he perceives how the one may be deduced from the other, and so on. If the co-ordination between our own mental elements and the elements of the environment is reproduced once more in ourselves, we are "conscious" of it. This happens, for instance, when the intensity, the origin and the aim of our impulses and drives are well known to us. Such an insight into our mental mechanism we call "consciousness," which represents an autonomous system by itself. The faculty of human consciousness, which may be considerably developed by proper training, has erected a kind of barrier between man and animal, engendering many misconceptions and errors. The animal, too, might know of its environment, and the bird building its nest might know what it builds, how it builds, and what immediate gratification the action serves. Most probably, however, animals do not know or understand the more remote purposes of things and do not practice introspection.

Psychological phenomena furnish us with the possibility of testing the concept of the organic image in regard to human society. The predominant primary forces of the soma, such as hunger, the sexual instinct, the urge of activity, the love of freedom, and the instinct of self-preservation are associated in the human being with forces induced from the outside, from the cognition of the environment. The human individual recognizes the desires and necessities of his fellow beings and is in a position to arrange his behavior accordingly. Thus, for instance, the exchange of goods and the division of labor become comprehensible, which, by gratifying the wishes of our fellow beings, at the same time gratify our own instincts and desires. Thus specialized trades, professions, and social classes come into being and the subdivisions and differentiations within animal communities are explainable.

On the strength of the psychophysical co-ordination proposed in the Appendix, the concept of an "entirety" or "whole" may find an explanation. The "ego" or "I," the soul, the psyche, the consciousness appear to us to be an indivisible entity. This is comprehensible from a physical aspect, considering that there are uniform systems not only in nature, but even in physics. Complete natural entities become particularly evident when recurrent changes, like the steady functioning of metabolism, are considered. We need not, therefore, be surprised that living beings, besides their physical individuality, should also be endowed with a uniform mentality the culmination of whose development results in personality.

Interesting conclusions result from the fact that we have co-ordinated sensations and emotions to the relative speed of relaxation of physical tension. If this is correct, feelings of *pleasure and pain should, on the whole, compensate each other,* as any increase of satisfaction is followed by a corresponding discomfort. This statement seems to be contradicted by the fact that we distinguish different human types according to the emotion in apparent predominance. The healthy, cheerful, and happy people on the one hand and the sick, embittered, melancholy, and unhappy on the other. It is, however, erroneous to believe that the specific feeling, whether pleasure or pain, is always predominant in these persons, for anybody suffering pain is glad at its cessation or even abatement. Such alleviation is a source of pleasure to him not available to others. What actually distinguishes these human types is the extent of satisfaction which may constantly lift or lower them to another level for satisfaction.

We have not yet clearly stated what constitutes the difference between body and soul, a question that has greatly preoccupied men's minds at all times and is still so doing. Is one of these phenomena primary and the other secondary or are they but two aspects of the same thing, or does only one of the two acutally and in truth exist, the other being a mere illusion? Should we profess dualism, monism, idealism, materialism, or still some other kind of ism?

Although we consider such questions irrelevant to this treatise, we will not shirk an answer: *the relation between body and soul necessarily is the same as the relation between the content of cognition and cognition itself.* The content of a cognition is physical, cognition itself is psychological or mental. Both are obviously real and not illusory. Furthermore, both are, in a certain sense, identical and, at best, to be distinguished in respect of concept only. Just as any cognition comes into existence through its content — and through its content alone — so is every emotion exclusively determined by its physical counterpart. Nothing will remain of a cognition that is deprived of its content and as little of an experience devoid of its physical counterpart. Whether we maintain that nothing exists in the universe but experiences, the physical phenomena representing nothing but a part thereof, or whether we believe body and soul to be but two aspects of a third factor, called God, creator, or nature, is of no particular importance. These are formulations incapable of being made the foundation of sound scientific research at the present stage of human knowledge.

CHAPTER IV

SPECIAL PROPERTIES
OF THE ORGANIC IMAGE

1. *The Extent of the Organic Image*

Now to be considered is the extent to which our concept of organic image is applicable to monoplasts living singly or in communities. And even with these we shall have to assume the existence of some kind of limited or primitive image, for their behavior in reacting to their environment is essentially similar to that of the higher animals. It is evidently next to impossible to draw a rigid boundary between man and monoplast. Besides, it is a principle of scientific argument to apply a faculty, relation, or feature, to similar conditions to the farthest extent possible. Extrapolation is applied and its results are turned to account as a working hypothesis until they prove inadequate.

The difference between a monoplast and a primitive human being sometimes appears as vast as that which exists between individuals of the human race; but this does not, however, affect the basic principle. In all cases where the organism intelligently and of its own accord adapts its behavior to its environment, the source of such behavior must be sought in the internal reproduction of the environmental system alone. Such a view is justifiable in particular wherever the organism is endowed not only with metabolic organs, but also with sensory and effector organs.

The reproductive faculty of individual cells is of special moment with regard to the group of cells representing tissues or organs. An agreement in respect to a common behavior of all these cells is arrived at by means of an interchange of reproductions. This occurs most markedly in the nervous system, a property which is not limited to this particular organ of transmission only. Plants apparently lack a central organ of reproduction and control, although they possess projection apparatus, like leaves and root-hairs, comparable to the sensory organs and the nervous system of the animals. The life of plants has evolved on different lines from that of animals. Nevertheless, they consist of cells, so that which was said concerning monoplasts is at least valid with respect to plants also. The close contiguity of cells creates a subtle relation that permits a transmission of impressions from cell to cell. Plants possess properties that in an intensified degree belong to the nervous system of the animals. Consider the sensitive mimosa, in this connection. It is well known that there are not only energetic but also substantial intercellular protoplasmic connections in plants. Their great difference from animals consists only in the fact that specialization has been effected without any special development of projection apparatus. We shall return to this problem in the next paragraph which treats of the structure of the organisms.

But it is quite possible also, in principle at least, to further extend our conclusions to apply in a like manner to other self-maintaining systems, to genes and viruses or to atoms and molecules. According to our view, which is in no way contradicted by experience, the basic elements of living matter are likewise living matter. This sentence, in the nature of a recursion formula, forces us, in its last consequence, to regard molecules as well as their component parts as living matter, so that logically our view as put forth above should also be valid in respect to the latter. An extrapolation with regard to the so-called hierarchic principle of biology is, incidentally, conducive to the same inference, namely, *that life, in the widest sense of the concept, has no limits in the direction of the infinitesimal.*

If within a group of atoms or molecules an electron is displaced by a new supply of energy, on its return to the original state a quantity of inferior energy — a photon of lower frequency — is emitted. This represents a typical "metabolic process." Another of the kind is the Compton process. When a photon is emitted because an electron returns to its original condition, an autonomous action of the atom, a "bio-reaction," occurs. Consequently atoms and molecules are also to be considered as active-autonomous centers of specific life-like activity, of assimilation and expulsion, and, more than this, the active control of metabolism does not seem to be at all the mysterious and exclusive privilege of the organic. Atoms are "born," for they exist; they "die" of old age, and can be "killed," as may be observed under favorable conditions. First and foremost, atoms and molecules possess the faculty of autonomous regeneration: if an electron is forcibly ejected from its respective group, the atom or the molecule will always try to replenish itself.*

If we wish to explain the faculty of life, we can do so only by proving the existence of life in the so-called inorganic sphere also, thus conceiving it in the light of a universal principle. The author is of opinion that it is not sufficient to develop our physicochemical knowledge in the direction of biology, it is just as important to apply biological principles to chemistry and physics — considering the self-maintaining systems of the microcosm in the biological sense, as the living individuals of communities. We are forced today to acknowledge that the essential features and peculiarities of life are not to be found in plants and animals only, but are also recognizable in a variety of other autonomous or self-maintaining systems, such as atoms, molecules, and crystals. *Without doing violence to our imagination, we can well "visualize" atoms and molecules as representing "organisms" on another level of evolution.* Incidentally, the conception

---

* "However complex a molecule may be, however large the number of electrons it may contain, there seems to be an "awareness" by each electron of what all others are doing and a strict adherence to the rule that no two must play the same role at the same time. No theoretical proof has been given of this exclusion principle. . . . There seems here to be some aspect of nature of great philosophic content beyond the understanding of the physicist." (from J. Lennard-Jones, "New Ideas in Chemistry," *Scientific Monthly,* Vol. 80, No. 3, 1955).

that all things are animate, albeit in varying degree, was originally advanced by the great German philosopher Leibnitz about three hundred years ago.

Be that as it may, he who holds that life and its self-maintaining functions cease where our visual observation is obstructed, as regards the infinitesimal by the deficiencies of the microscope, should be obliged to prove so radical a limit. It would be difficult indeed to persuade us of the actual existence and intrinsic necessity of so significant a rupture of nature precisely at a point remarkable merely because of the peculiarity of knowledge and our technique. The limit of our tools is constantly shifting in accordance with technical progress and has recently changed again by the invention of the electron microscope. The origination of organisms and their evolution necessitates the participation and co-operation of all the stages of organization right down to the minutest particles.

2. *The Structure of the Organic Image*

Every cell, and even the components of a cell, such as protoplasm, nucleus, centrosomes, and so on, represents a more or less limited reproduction of its environment, since any animate structure down to the very minutest possesses an image of the environment peculiar to itself. Wherever there is organic matter, there also is the reproductive substratum, which consequently densely fills up all living matter. Although this substratum completely permeates the entire space occupied by the organisms, it nevertheless has a structure of its own, just as the substance of material of the earth has a structure of its own. The latter, to mention only its coarser structure, is subdivided into atmosphere, hydrosphere, biosphere, and lithosphere, which again possess finer structures of their own. The fact that the biosphere and lithosphere show strongly marked structures peculiar to themselves presents the biologist and the geologist with many difficult problems. We are especially interested at present in the biosphere. We accordingly subdivide all living matter into populations, biocoenoses, states, communities, peoples, tribes, herds, flocks, hives, swarms, heaps, organims, organs, tissues, cells, nuclei, chromosomes, genes, and so on. There is a gradationed structure of reproductive units in biology possessing an organization in the nature of a super-order.

We are now confronted with the problem of making definite statements about the structure of the organic image which pervades the entire body. In the continual chain, be-ginning with an external sensory irritation or excitation and ending in external action, junctions are always passed that not only represent collecting centers of the vast number of sense impressions but also the controlling centers for the actions of the effector organs. The main junction is the brain, the gray cortex of the cerebrum in particular, to which a part of the spinal cord, as well as subcortical centers, may al-so be counted.

Though the whole organism as such, with all its com-ponent elements, constitutes the substratum of organic repro-duction, it is nevertheless possible that separate parts of the body are distinguished by more distinct, concentrated, com-prehensive, and permanent reproductive power than other parts. And just as we subdivide organic matter according to its functions into separate units, or units nested, as it were, one within the other, we are able to define certain units per-forming their respective specialized functions within the entire, all-comprehensive organic image. Thus the result is a superimposed order of reproductions or images, an order identical with the hierarchic order of life.

Such a specialized reproductive unit has already been particularly pointed out, viz. the brain, for the brain, with its 10 to 15 billion interconnected nerve cells, unlike other organs, uses the whole body as an instrument. In the chromo-somes of the nucleus the whole genealogy is depicted in a more or less unbroken continuity. The existence and nature of these images are revealed not so much in their origin, but rather in their amazing efficacy, which become manifest in the reproduction of conditions long since past. In a cell the nucleus — not absent even in bacteria — is decidedly the most important specialized substratum of the central image, quite similar to the brain.

At this juncture we may obviously ask how the exceedingly large number of images, of which there is one in each elemental unit of any animate structure, possibly could combine into one single image determinative of the behavior of the whole organism. That is to say, for instance, that the reproductive powers of separate genes combine into the reproductive power of the entire chromosome chain, and these again into the organic image of the whole cell, and so forth. We will first discuss this fundamental question by using an analogy for illustration. Imagine a taut string, for example, each molecule of which performs a well-defined movement upon any given impetus, yet does not interfere with the uniform vibration or undulatory motion of the whole string.

Generally speaking, any constructive combination of two or more units may result in a new and novel unit. The superposition of two waves results in a suspended wave of quite different properties from those of the initial waves; a certain combination of sodium and chloride results in common salt, which is something quite unlike its components; separate notes can be combined into a melody of absolutely new qualities; and a planned combination of mosaic stones results in a symmetrical pattern. Thus a combination of separate organic images may result in a new and novel image, with functions, tensions, forces, and a rhythm of its own. The structural combination of two or more units may create a new unit, entity, entirety, or structure, the properties of which cannot be inferred from the properties of their structural elements. Several such newly formed units may combine anew into a still more extensive and comprehensive entity. A mixture of gaseous oxygen and hydrogen, for instance, does not constitute an organized entity, as there are no interrelations between the atomic groups of oxygen and those of hydrogen. Therefore, also, any part taken separately exhibits the same properties. If two atoms of hydrogen combine with one atom of oxygen to form water, newly organized groups of three atoms each have come into being. However, considering all these separate molecules, we again have a mere "quantity of matter." Assuming that the molecules form an ice crystal, we again obtain an organized and superordinated structure.

In order to gain still another idea of what the organic image is like, let us compare it to a library. A library represents an accumulation of pictures or images in the shape of books, which are generally not crammed together chaotically but have been systematically arranged and registered according to certain principles. Though each of the books contains a reproduced system of the past and present environment, their order and sequence likewise represent a system, namely, the image of a plan. This plan has been devised in the central office of the library where there are catalogues, indexes, and every sort of record covering the contents of the library. All these, in their turn, furnish a picture of the whole library, which in functional respects entirely differs from the totality of images contained therein. The main office or brain-center has connections and means of communication with the external world, such as a telephone, postal service, and others, and last but not least with its personnel, headed by a chief librarian.

Every single book, which we may think of as representing a cell of an individual organism, has passively participated in the organization of the central image. All the books are also subjected to its supervision or control, the latter directing the discarding of unsuitable ones, ordering the acquisition of new ones, determinging their place within the system of the library, and so on. The remarkable structure, consisting of an accumulation of all these images, discloses a systematic order of the same kind and consequence quite similar to the systematic order contained by any living organisms.

3. *The Functions of the Organic Image*

The functions of organic matter are partly passive and partly active. The passive functions consist mainly in the receiving of impressions by means of the receptive apparatus. These impressions are comparable to mosaic stones, which if correctly arranged, reproduce the energetic fields governing the environment. These impressions — sensations, according to the terminology of psychology — are obviously necessary if a more or less correct reproduction is to result.

Although the passive receiving of external influences is the basic condition for the existence of an organic image, this is by no means its only function. It is endowed with an autonomous or self-maintaining independence which manifests itself in a primary tendency toward certain vital processes. These primary forces are tending toward active changes, such as dissipation of energy, increase of stability and harmony, and so on. Physiologically, they result in the unceasing processes of metabolism. By way of suitable projection apparatus linked with these processes, one part of the primary forces takes on the nature of an excitant behind organic activity of various kinds. Their activating effect may be increased by means of appropriate technical devices or tools. We all know what effect is produced by pressing a button that closes an electrical circuit. The action may even unleash a world war.

Conscious activity is exhibited first of all in a certain preparation for the passive receiving of impressions; attention, observation, looking, listening, and so on, are active manifestations. The re-arrangement of separate impressions into a systematically correct image of the environment mostly occurs actively, a fact we experience in mental work with its accompanying effort and fatigue. A purely inner activity is one that is best observable from within, for instance, thought, imagination, mental creation, or dreaming. The extent to which some functions are passive or active manifestations is doubtful. Remembering, inner maturation, and a brain wave are such instances.

It may happen that one organism selects as means for reproduction another organism from the manifold structures out of the environment. This action is of great moment in human society. We learn from our fellow beings through the medium of the written and the spoken word. This means that their mental or brain structure is partly transferred to our brain. In this manner, the reproduction of an image may be repeated at will in numerous organisms.

Having discussed first the passive receiving of images, for example, in the case of pupil and teacher, we must now point out that the reverse may also happen, that is, an individual organism may also actively form and mold the environment by inducing already-existing images to become similar to itself. In human society, this happens by instruction, influence, suggestion, information, and so forth. Our own organic image may be radiated in various directions simultaneously through the medium of a speech, a lecture, or the publication of a literary work, as a book or pamphlet, or in a newspaper, or by spreading a rumor by word of mouth.

Finally, there is the possibility of a reciprocity of influence from organism to organism. An immediate interchange of the contents of images may occur, for instance, in question and answer. Man disposes in his power of speech and technical resources of excellent means of transmitting the contents of images, even across vast distances, so that it may be assumed that the mental or brain structure of most coeval people will be analogous in the main points.

In regard to animals, we are not so well informed in this respect as we do not master their "language" so thoroughly. We may nevertheless infer the existence of a considerable capacity for the transmission and reception of communications, from the behavior of herds and other animal communities, which is mostly the same under similar conditions, as, for instance, in their reaction to danger. The method of communication of bees and ants has been almost completely solved by man. An analogous transmission of cellular images from cell to cell within a group of cells is facilitated by their protoplasmic contact, the intercellular connection being so close that the essential characteristics of the organic images are reciprocally transmitted among vicinal cells, so that an impression caused by an irritation may be communicated not only to the whole organ, but also to the entire organism. There is throughout a "suggestive correspondence."

Extensive specialization of physical or somatic functions leads to a division of work and the development of specific organs. Cells transmitting a received impression without much change or modification combine into chains and cords serving solely as a means of communication, which are defined as nerves. These transmit the communications to certain centers of reproduction and control in the body. Such a center is, for example, the subcortical center behind the eye, which controls, or "steers," most optic functions arising from impressions received. The autonomous control of the mediatory image comes also into action if the external system is received and reflected again. An independent action of organic images happens, for instance, if a gym squad is counting off, each person calling to his neighbor the number following the one heard.

A special form of propagation of images is multiplication. An organic image can produce similar images, thus multiplying almost illimitably. The constant joint multiplication of two individual cells — the egg cell (ovum) and the male cell (spermatozoon) — will result in a new organism consisting of innumerable cells. The organisms may in their turn multiply in a like manner. The stages of development of the fecundated egg disclose the efficaciousness of this kind of propagation.

Thus it may be said that organic images or organisms are molded and formed in two ways. In the one instance, autonomous psychological processes and external impressions may modify an already existing image by structural changes of its system. The center of control is the impressionable, exceedingly complex brain, which assimilates and associates new elements with every new impression. In the other instance, entirely new organic images are created by composition and formation of their basic elements. This is typical of new images originating in the almost unchanged germinative cells.

4. *The Explanation of Fitness*

The living organism is a product of its past and present environment. The organic reproductive power we have termed "organic image" is created by sensory organs and their corresponding transmission apparatus, while it also transforms its environment by actions through the medium of effector organs. The environment thus forming the organism, and vice versa, a reciprocation is established. Evidently neither is independent of the other as to structure and function, but inseparably linked by a considerable mutual influence. The interlacement of processes of the organism with those of the outer world, as demonstrated by the concept of the organic image, results in that peculiarity in the behavior of organisms termed fitness, finality, design, directiveness, purposiveness, expediency and so forth.

Before embarking upon an explanation of these terms, all of which more or less express the same concept, we will briefly touch upon the linguistic side. The eye and the brain are the instruments of reproduction best developed and most familiar to us and therefore it seems advisable to use the terminology used in reference to them for our purposes. Such expressions as "to see clearly and distinctly," "a narrow or a wide horizon," "farsighted," or "transparent" should be generally used for any kind of reproduction of the environment. And as the visual power of the eye can be intensified or extended by means of optical instruments not only in the direction of the remote — by a telescope — but also in respect to the minute — by a magnifying glass or a microscope — man is also capable of "extending his horizon." If the brain is not directed toward the receiving of the environment, we may be said to "shut our eyes." In this reverse case, the cognition of certain relations of the environment might be called "insight" or "perception." Shortsightedness is a kind of deficiency in optical reproduction. However, this special term is well applicable in a general sense to any human individual exhibiting an analogous deficiency of reproduction in other respects also. It is likewise possible to speak of "clairvoyance" in a general sense.

As the organism contains the system of the reproduced environment, every change of the environment, recognized as such, changes the organism too, and in the reverse respect an autonomous change of the organism is possible only if the environment is analogously changed, which is effected by virtue of the activities released by the organic image. Mankind has changed his environment to a large extent. On the other hand, the repercussion of this created environment on man constantly produces new organic images. Consider only the influence of homes, schools, nationality, religion, technology, and social life. Anyone who is not a victim of self-deception, but strives to see his respective wishes really fulfilled, has no choice but to act in a manner which will ultimately so mold or change his environment that it will produce the desired image in himself. Environment and organism are, at any rate, conjoined to such a degree that any event in either of them automatically affects the other. This reciprocal change of original and image by means of projection and reaction or of action and reaction is elucidated by the following examples.

The watchmaker repairing a watch is actuated by the forces of the organic image demanding sense and harmony. He can appease the desire evoked of the organic image only by producing the desired effect in his surroundings. A satisfactory solution by a dream, by imagination, or even a hallucination is neither complete nor lasting. To achieve this, the respective systems of original and reproduction or image must infallibly be made to agree. In the present case that is realizable only by making the watch go. Let us turn to the artist, whose creative work is based on the same phenomenon. He, too, attains the intended harmony of his inherent organic image by a corresponding transformation or new formation of the external original.

Whereas the four-dimensional system of the environment is reproduced by the three-dimensional organism, the present events of the organism in their turn are projected or reflected back into the four-dimensional environment. Or, to express it differently, the changes of the environment in the past and the future correspond to actual changes of the organism in the present time. This three-dimensional reproduction of the events occurring in the four-dimensional environment may also be defined as the "plan" or "design" of these said events. Thus the present system of reproduction or organic image contains the design or template of the system of the environment extending in space *and* time: *the corresponding events in environment and organism are not synchronal, but take place in different dimensions.*

The fact that future events are already contained in the present individual or organism is explainable in the following manner: as the organic image contains the past, the laws of nature are fixed in it, and must consequently also embrace future events as far as they are rooted in experience and logic. Psychologically expressed, this means that the organism, knowing the past, is able to draw conclusions about the future by means of its reason. The organism need not at all be conscious of this process. The male stag-beetle larva, providing space for the big mandibles of its last stage of insect development, is certainly not conscious of the connection between its present actions and the future purpose of its efforts. Its knowledge, which has originated in the course of innumerable generations during the evolution of its species, is concerned with the present moment only. It is recorded by the genotype together with the complete plan of organization. Compare instinctive actions, for instance. The interconnection of environment and organism represents a mechanism which is automatically and expediently adapting the individual to the four-dimensional environment.

As regards the final, teleological event, the behavior of the organism is only apparently determined by the future. In reality, as we have seen above, it is always predetermined by the past. This becomes obvious if we consider future conditions that seem to be the cause of fitness. Here we observe that expedient directiveness or organic behavior merely represents *repetition or recurrence of former condi-*

tions already rooted in the organism, i.e. in the organic image. For instance, the great planetary orbits and rhythms take care of the constant repetition of many terrestrial phenomena, such as day and night, the seasons, and the tides, as we noted heretofore.

Future events without analogy or precedent in the past history of the organism are not capable of evoking expedient behavior in the latter. An organism hit by a meteor falling from the sky cannot take any expedient precautionary measures, as such an event cannot be recorded. But organisms take precautions against the approach of winter, thus continuing a periodicity already rooted in the organic image. This becomes more clear when clothed in psychological terminology, which puts it like this: future conditions produce fitness of behavior only if the organism can prognosticate them in accordance with past impressions and experiences.*

The interaction of invironment and organism includes the concept that the final effect of an action simultaneously is its cause. Since the three-dimensional organic reproduction of the four-dimensional environment coincides in the present time, the statement that the cause of a need is also at the same time the very cause of its satisfaction represents the correct conclusion. The immediate satisfaction of a need represents an attempt by the individual to approach a temporally and spatially remote aim in the environment. Whatever occurs in the organic image at any given moment is reflected into the entire four-dimensional or space-time environment, thus affecting the future also.

5. *Free Energy of the Organisms and Metabolism*

One of the most astonishing properties of organisms is the faculty to dispose ever anew of free energy, although this energy is constantly being degraded or dissipated by metabolism and by other activities.

---

* Fitness actually is a cybernetic feedback process — the property of being able to adjust future conduct on a basis of past performance, in addition to information storage.

In order to operate with free energy, we should make use of isothermal changes, i.e. changes occurring at a constant temperature, but it is also sufficient if the same temperature governs the initial and the final state of a cyclic process. We may use the terms "free energy" or "available energy" if we consider the ever-recurrent changes of natural phenomena, since free energy is then degraded or dissipated proportionally to the increase of entropy. In our everyday life we are more familiar with free energy, mostly in the form for which we have to pay, viz. food, fuel, electric power, and, last but not least, money itself. For reasons of explicitness, we frequently prefer the term "degradation of energy," or "dissipation of energy," to that of "increase of entropy." We do this because of the close relation of entropy to free energy.*

In degrading free or available energy, organisms as well as machines use part of it either for the performance of work or for the accumulation of more free energy, which may be utilized again in later work. Certain work is always necessary to provide free energy from the environment for renewed utilization. A steam engine or an internal combustion engine sets in motion the valves, the petrol pump, the engine-governor, the distributor, the regulator, and so on, all serving to supply new energy, or to overcome the deadlock by using up mechanical inert energy, and the like. The actual performance is constantly fed back to controls which automatically make corrections. This construction provides for the uninterrupted continuance of its operation and the supply of new energy, thus representing the prototype of every self-maintaining system we have proved in Part One. The originator of such an ingeniously designed contrivance is man, whereas that which takes care of his own uninterrupted metabolism is the organic image.

Man, for instance, often enough performs unpleasant work "by the sweat of his brow," being fully conscious that by doing so he is earning his living. "Living" stands here as a general term for any free or available energy advancing his

---

*$E—TS=F$, wherein E represents the total energy of a system, T the temperature, S the entropy and F the free energy.

own metabolism, including money, food, commodities, and the like. The underlying fundamental law is perhaps best exhibited in its simplest form by communicating vertical tubes. The liquid in the one arm can yield to the pressure of gravity only if it is performing work by lifting the liquid in the other arm. Analogous to the sinking of the liquid in one tube, which accompanies its rising in the other, is the phenomenon that any increase of free energy is necessarily accompanied by a greater loss of free energy, so that the final result always represents an increase of entropy.

In order to visualize the metabolic process more clearly, let us consider some organism, say, a caterpillar. All through his life, he must eat his way through the world, so to speak. He assimilates innumerable components of other individuals, which spatially pass through him. He is ever cramming strange universes into his system — air, water, electromagnetic energy, animal and vegetable substances — and all this with an extraordinary average constancy. If we were confronted with the whole mass at once, we would be not a little surprised at the quantity. In front, the entire amount of food for a lifetime; and behind, an endless waste of refuse. This, we might say, "catalytic" property of the organism to degrade energy uninterruptedly — practically without the basic structure of the organism being changed — is termed "steady state," "transient equilibrium," or "homeostasis." An organism is, so to speak, a vessel into which free energy is flowing in a more or less constant rhythm, and which is emitting degraded energy, on condition, of course, that there is an unlimited store of energy, an inexhaustible reservoir of free energy in the surrounding space, or a continually regenerating environment supplying the organism with ever-new energy (air, food, water, heat, and the like.)

We may observe a similar metabolism not only with organisms, but also with any other self-maintaining systems, like atoms, molecules and stars. An atmospheric atom assimilating a photon and returning it with a lower frequency to the environment, or the earth assimilating solar energy and reflecting it back into space, performs a metabolic process. The inner metabolism of the earth has repeatedly been treated of in scientific literature. All these systems are of the nature of constantly working machines at maximum efficiency.

The steady degradation of energy by metabolism does not merely appear as an aim or purpose of life, which in turn should only serve as a means to some other end. It rather seems that *the continuance of metabolism is in itself an end nature is aiming at, either directly or indirectly,* and which therefore cannot be absent in any organism. From birth to maturation, organisms continually accumulate stores of free energy. This accumulation represents no "luxury"; it rather serves the direct increase of metabolism, that is to say, it serves the intensity of vital functions and is its source. In some instances the preservation of the germ plasm and the evolution of the species have been mentioned as the ultimate purpose of organisms. However, it must be pointed out that this does not contradict the above statement, as the preservation of the germ plasm coincides with the continuity of metabolism, and the evolution of the species with its intensification.

A means to the preservation of life is the perfection of the organic image, that is, to increase the fitness of organisms, which would also comprise the increase of knowledge, the augmentation of mental powers, and the promotion of civilization and culture, all of which are mostly held to be in themselves nature's aim and purpose.

6. *Dysteleology, or the Unfitness in Nature*

Certain organic events often seem senseless, as, for instance, the formation of two or more heads or tails after an injury, a phenomenon often discussed relative to the subject. Such inexpedient superregeneration does not, however, represent a direct opposite to fitness, but rather its limitation. It implies a deficiency of fitness, presupposing a restricted reproductive faculty. Instead of contradicting, dysteleology is rather a confirmation of fitness and organic directiveness, and there is no difficulty in proving this.

First of all, it must be pointed out that there is no fitness or unfitness as such. Every event is expedient only to a certain degree, being at the same time inexpedient to some extent. An established fitness remains so only within certain limits, and transgressing, it may become unfit. Therefore, we are not so much concerned with a possibly existing fitness as with the possible limits or extent of fitness.

In a former paragraph we have explained fitness as the faculty of the organic to reproduce environment. The extent of this actual reproduction cannot be without consequence to the extent of fitness as such, since the environment cannot be reproduced either completely or faultlessly. Any deficiency, incompleteness, or faultiness of reproduction or image must necessarily impair the expediency of the organic behavior, so that in practice an ideal fitness is unattainable. Obviously, any animal behavior may at best be fit within the correctly recognized or reproduced section of the environment. We are quite familiar with this phenomenon within the sphere of consciousness. Insofar as we consciously wish to act expediently, it is quite plain to us that we can do so only on the basis of our cognitions.

Our conscious behavior can be expedient merely to the extent of foresight, since we are not prepared for unforeseen events. This inexpediency may generally be traced to the deficiency of the organic reproduction and transmission apparatus. The organism behaves inexpediently if the future environment is not contained in the organic reproduction owing to lack of experience or insight. The organic reproduction can also be incorrect or wrong, which likewise would affect fitness in a particular manner; we speak of errors, mistakes, delusions, and the like, in such cases. To what extent the fitness will suffer through such mental conditions needs no further comment. The attainment of an end presupposes distinct and correct cognitions.

If dysteleology is explainable by shortsightedness and errors with regard to conscious actions, defects in the organic image must be assumed to exist in the sphere of unconscious or subconscious actions also. We may, for instance, speak of ignorance as to the environment if the organism is transferred into completely new surroundings. The organism may obtain a certain limited knowledge about the future just as man knows about the future progress of stars from their past behavior. Accordingly, the actual behavior of organisms leading to fitness presupposes an extensive continuity of the environment, the changes of which are of a periodical or rhythmical nature. Thus, lack of knowledge, or knowledge that is not confirmed by recurrence, must impair fitness. Summing up, we may state that the existence of apparent unfitness in biology results from the concept of fitness itself, and is only a matter of definition.

We now touch upon an important consequence of the organic image of interest to not only the scientific world but to every thinking person. We are here concerned with certain apparently misguided or biologically inadequate forms of human society, whose most disquieting manifestations are found in the authoritarian and totalitarian state. Such "social dysteleologies" arise in exactly the same way as do similar defects of the organic image we have discussed in Chapter II, 3, that is, from a nonuniform, incomplete, or incorrect reproduction of the space-time environment, including national history. And the future development of such defective social structures generally are ended by natural selection, just as, for example, animals having two or more heads or tails are eliminated.

Chapter V

RESULTS

1. *The Definition of Life*

On the basis of the foregoing exposition we may now formulate the following definition of life:

Life is the active faculty of self-maintaining systems to reproduce the space-time environment in the present all at once and systematically true as regards its fields of force, including its chemistry. Life has the additional faculty of speeding up catalytically the process of energy degradation.

This definition states that the active behavior of organisms automatically takes the reproduced, i.e. the recognized, environment into consideration, in this way becoming ever adapted to the environment. Adaption in turn leads to fitness, directiveness, purposiveness, and so on.

The objection might be raised that a photographic film represents a physiochemical structure with properties quite similar to those of the organism. By a protracted exposure of the film the environment extending in time can likewise be projected and fixed in the present time, the consecutive light impressions being successively superimposed upon it. The color film, too, reproduces an image of the entire environment.

And yet the two differ markedly. The photographic film has not actively acquired its reproductive faculty and is therefore not able to change or transform it by some active interference of its own. Moreover, it does not possess any organs by means of which it might change the environment. It lacks metabolism by which to change catalytically the process of degradation of energy, and thus lacks the main faculty of life. The photographic film has not been created by its component elements, nor do its reproductive properties serve its component elements, which alone could actively regenerate the film. This results in the very limited, i.e. uniplicate, reproductive faculty of the photographic film, which can not regenerate of itself. Reciprocal interaction and harmony as existing between the living individual and environment are absent in the photographic film.

Our definition of life might still be criticized as being incomplete, because it merely states the peculiarity of organisms without touching upon the cause. This problem, however, is no longer a question concerning the nature of life, but that of life's origin and the formation of the organisms. We propose to treat of this in the following Section, although the problem has already been discussed in a more general way in Part One.

2. *The Origin of Life, or the Formation of Organisms and Communities*

We may assume as a certainty that the origin of all organisms ever was and will be fundamentally the same in the entire biosphere, and in fact in the whole universe, and that it has occurred analogously to the formation of communities open to our inspection. The formation of a group of cells of an animal colony or village community affords a convenient insight. In all these cases it is the living components themselves that, by their complementary processes, give birth to the greater units, multiplying, specializing, and organizing their organic images in such a way that larger, more comprehensive organic images result. This process is termed "association." Nature's most ingenious trick is *association, with its unending line of consequences* — the unification of elementary units or individuals into communities in which alone the faculties of the former find an opportunity for all development.

The following simple experiment may be of interest in this connection. A freshwater sponge is ground and the pulp squeezed through a rag, by which process a large number of separate cells is obtained. These isolated cells will now be observed to move by themselves toward one another and unite into plasmodia, which give rise to new sponges. This, indeed, is a remarkable illustration of how isolated cells reunite to form a new specimen of the species. The isolated cells and groups of cells merge into a new cell body, producing a new individual.

In any case, we always observe that living beings take their origin solely from other living beings. Every contemporary organism is the product of other organisms, of which the same thing may be said, a chain of causes thus leading back into the obscure past. We are obliged to judge of the province of the smallest systems known to us, like the atoms, molecules, genes, and viruses, by extending our conclusions derived from the observation of the formation of living units, such as communities, families, organizations, and the like. In this way we arrive at the conclusion that *life·never originated from nonliving matter and has never spontaneously come into being. It rather is an immanent property of even the smallest individuals, the atoms and the molecules, to be introduced into superordinated systems by association.*

We could try to explain our meaning in more detail by referring to a rural community open to our inspection. A group of persons without regard for one another's interests is not to be considered as representing a living or organized unit, although each individual lives. As long as the individuals are mutually indifferent or even antagonistic, they do not represent a uniform body or organism. Only the mutual induction of forces creating relations among the individuals calls into being a new living unit with a definite boundary and a new inner content, that is to say, an organized unit.

Should a group of people unite and organize, for instance, into a village community with typical vital functions, then phenomena like growth, the birth of a new village, topographic adjustment, regeneration of particular trades and professions, differentiation, self-regulation, and so on, will automatically come into being. In exactly the same way, every living being originates exclusively through the medium of living components.

A crowd of people, say, slaves, prisoners, a ship's passengers, the customers of a shop, hotel, or restaurant, a shipwrecked crew, or a group of refugees, is no more alive than a table or any other such object. A table could never become a living whole even though each of its molecules should have to be considered as such, for the interaction of the mutual influences which only are producing living structures is lacking. This does not exclude the possibility of unorganized aggregates suddenly manifesting vitality. Such may be the case when a heterogeneous crowd, guided from without, organizes, exhibits co-ordinated activity, revolts and displays some vital functions of its own. The fact that some material recrystallizes, undergoes oxidation, becomes magnetic, forms eddies, may be regarded as the first faint sign of life.

The psychological view enables us to apply by generalization the conditions we are familiar with in human society to other organisms also. The natural tendencies of all human beings are more or less similar and their fundamental knowledge is roughly the same. But according to whether a man grows up on a farm, in a mining district, or in a town, he is influenced by his surroundings, and becomes either a farmer, a miner, or a townsman. Consciousness is generally of little account in this kind of specialization. If a man's education has already progressed in a particular direction, he will, on a change of residence, endeavor to find surroundings congenial to his disposition, developing his talents in the meantime; that is to say, the farmer will incline toward the country, the miner toward a mining district, and the intellectual worker toward a town. No one will change his profession for trifling reasons. The citizen's early development is locally determined, his future education or training, however, is influenced by his origin.

Within a certain stage of organization, the formation of an organism may have taken place in the following manner: a village community eliminates some individuals capable of progeneration as "germs," which, joining anew, multiply, educate, and may form a new village community in a strange land. In order to obtain such a result, it is necessary that the surplus individuals should first be born within the old village community.

The same is true with regard to an individual animal producing pregnancy, thus forming a new organism. The fact that this process does not occur outside but within the parental womb makes no essential difference. The origin of sex cells may be assumed to have occurred in an analogous manner from their respective component elements, but on a lower level of development.

Human society with its rather complex structure develops automatically. The individual human being surveys a small circle only, his limited knowledge makes him play the role allotted to him as best he can, and regeneration, adaptation, regulation, and the like, become inevitable. The elaborate structure of the organism arises quite analogously from the automatic and harmonious interaction of individual cells. The field of vision of the individual cell is as limited as the wisdom of the individual human being, both behaving, to a certain degree, selfishly.

Specialization on the part of the individuals, caused not only by their disposition — talents, abilities, inclinations, financial means, and so on — but also by their relations to the entirety, results in an essentially new organization embracing whole groups of persons, which is superimposed on the individual organization. The state, postal service, railway, stock exchange, clubs, trade unions, and the like, are organizations and associations of such origin. All these superordinated systems are endowed with a reproductive center or center of control, which may consist either of a group of individuals, such as the government, a managing committee, parliament, a board of directors, or of a single person — king, president, manager, chieftain, mayor, officer, and so on. In this comprehensible way, new living systems may emerge and evolve with definite limits and vital functions of their own.*

Any social order which strives to impress on its structural elements, i.e. its individuals, a new order from without, by force, just as an engineer designs and builds a machine for some particular purpose from dead materials and components, can never be regarded as a social order capable of evolution. For if everything is prescribed and regulated by the state from the individual's birth to his death, the individual can never, in response to his own sociological impulses, associate himself with other individuals or organizations, which is the only process by which new social life, in the widest sense of the word, can come into existence. If regulation, restitution, regeneration, and propagation are prescribed for the individual by the state, the whole structure will be nothing more than a kind of machine which, although it may exhibit a few lifelike functions, such as "metabolism" in the form of a bureaucratically regulated economy, will, like a machine, be subject to wear and tear. Component parts of the machine will constantly have to be replaced and "overhauled," a particularly impressive manifestation of which process can at present be observed in the so-called "purges," but the final destruction of the state-machine is thereby only postponed. The author is of the opinion that the laws of community formation must be respected in any and every social order; otherwise that order will perish. World history with its recurrent pattern of events supplies us with evidence in plenty to support this view.

---

* That life is a result of the mode of organization of matter has been recently discussed in an excellent paper by H. J. Muller, *Science*, Vol. 121, No. 3132, 1955.

APPENDIX

Systematization of Psychophysical Phenomena

1. *Classification of Elementary Experiences*

In order that psychophysical co-ordination shall be clearly understood, psychological phenomena or experiences shall be first divided into the following six elementary groups: *cognitions, instincts and impulses, tensions and stress, actions and passivity, satisfaction of wants, sensations or feelings of pleasure and of pain.* Some of these main groups shall in turn be subdivided.

1. *Cognitions* are subdivided as follows: (*a*) *sensations*, (*b*) *conceptions*, and (*c*) *perceptions*.

(*a*) *Sensations* include light and color, smell and taste, sound and hearing, heat and touch (or haptic sensations), and kinaesthetic sensations. In juxtaposition to the foregoing stand irritations and excitations.

(*b*) *Conceptions* include understanding, beliefs, opinions ideas, daydreams, delusions, illusions, hallucinations, thoughts, conclusions, inspirations, brain waves, memories, conjectures, presentiments, viewpoints, judgments, convictions, experiences, fancies, concepts, associations, suspicions, impressions, mistrust, and phantoms. The sum of our conceptions we define as knowledge, faith, and like convictions.

(*c*) *Perceptions* are a compound of sensations and conceptions, and are, therefore, not elementary but complex. The perception of a tree, for example, is the result of certain sensations, light or color sensations mostly, arousing associations and memories in the observer, which all together form the perception of the individual object, namely, the tree.

2. *Instincts and impulses, or "drives,"* may be enumerated without systemization as follows: impulses, greed, curiosity, inquisitiveness, desire, concupiscence, appetite, covetousness, craving, eagerness for activity (restlessness), wishes, hunger, thirst,

craving for freedom, instinct of self-preservation, need, longing, inclination, disposition, mania, likes and dislikes, expectancy, reluctance, repugnance, disgust, and aversion.

Volition or will power is a compound of different instincts, impulses, drives, and includes will, willfulness, choice, decision, wishes, desires, determination, wanting, schemes, intention, design, undertaking, and resolution.

3. *Tensions and stress* include questions, problems, tasks, enigmas, expectations, hopes, temptations, coercions, doubts, dilemmas, discord, excitement, conflict, bewilderment, and many other emotions.

4. *Actions* in general may be subdivided into (*a*) *mental activity* (*b*) *activity of performance* and (*c*) *passivity*.

(*a*) *Mental activity*, that is to say, the purely intellectual acts, includes thinking, judging, condemning, recollecting, remembering, combining, concluding, reflecting, inquiring, imagining, stating, comparing, recognizing, believing, having faith in, suspecting, mistrusting, learning, concentrating, paying attention, listening, watching, contemplating, selecting, deciding, impulses, understanding, opining, and assuming. Special forms include: calculating, composing, and many more.

(*b*) *Activity of performance* deals with complex processes in which psychic volition is associated with the physical events resulting from it. Some examples are working, doing, causing, moving, making, stirring, walking, talking, writing, exercising, eating, drinking, manufacturing, producing, shaking, trembling, behaving, watching, deciding, interfering, grasping, looking, taking care, anticipating, espying, exploring, tracing, lying in wait, and scrutinizing.

The various groups of actions are not always sharply defined one from another; even purely mental acts nearly always result in physical actions. Composing involves writing and playing; even the act of thinking can be accompanied by frowning.

(*c*) *Passivity* may be subdivided into (*ca*) *nonresistance* and (*cb*) *mental suffering*.

(*ca*) *Nonresistance* includes enduring, bearing, tolerating, forbearing, experiencing, trembling, falling asleep, awakening, and receiving.

(*cb*) *Mental suffering* includes insight, understanding, sensations, emotions, noticing, conceiving, recognizing, feeling, perceiving, becoming aware, inspirations, suppositions, thinking, presentiments, fancying, astonishment, bewilderment, and surprise.

5. *Satisfaction of wants* is of various kinds and includes contentment, satiation, the quenching of thirst, gratification, appeasement, pacification, relief, relaxation, liberation, release, and mitigation.

6. *Sensations or feelings of pleasure and of pain* include ease and comfort, well-being, serenity, agreeableness, pleasantness, beneficence, lust, enjoyment, joy, delight, bliss, cheerfulness, fun, rapture, ecstasy, sorrow, depression, melancholy, disharmony, pain, agony, anxiety, fear, terror, fright, shock, trepidation, coercion, distress, discomfort, trouble, danger, grief, wretchedness, and pity.

A variety of psychological phenomena denote the complexity of experience, like embarrassment, pride, passion, spitefulness, kindness, and cunning. A word list can be greatly extended, but the interpretation of a single word or concept is not insisted upon, as our systematization is open to modifications. We are primarily interested in demonstrating the fundamental idea that there are essentially different, reciprocally delimited, and distinctive groups of psychological phenomena.

2. *Some Characteristics of the Six Groups of Experiences*

Of the groups just defined, those classified *cognitions* are characterized by a content more or less remote in time and space. They furthermore possess a quality and a number of characteristics. They may be either right or wrong, distinct or dim, profound or superficial, comprehensive or particular, actively acquired or passively suffered, familiar or strange. Besides, cognitions of various kinds may easily occur simultaneously without encroaching upon each other, as, for instance, colors and some emotions, while others even fuse and blend to form new cognitions. Still others cannot coexist as, expressing contradictions, they cancel each other. Cognitions may be either stable or changeable.

Instincts and impulses and *tensions and stress* possess intensity and tendency. Two or more different impulses may dominate simultaneously, combining or complementing each other in such a way as to reinforce or weaken each other. Instincts and impulses drive toward an aim, their quality hence being defined. Besides aiming at the final end, they also tend toward all intermediate stages leading to its attainment and thus approaching it.

Volition or will power, too, exhibits strength and direction, and, like instincts and drives, aims at a definite end and its intermediate stages. But, contrary to the innumerable instincts and drives, every individual is in command of only one single will power at any given time.

Both *actions* and *passivity* are experienced directly. Like cognitions, they possess a quality and many other properties. A person may think either correctly or incorrectly, logically or illogically, clearly or vaguely, quickly or slowly, easily or laboriously, expediently or inexpediently; he may think of important or of unimportant things, of good or of bad things. Just as the drives and instincts are directed toward a final aim, so do actions of performance display a purpose. And just as instincts do not aim exclusively at the final end, but also at the attainment of the intermediate stages, so do actions include both the purpose proper and the means to its end.

Satisfaction of wants is positive and without tendency. It merely possesses quantity. The extreme case is absolute dissatisfaction.

Sensations or feelings are characterized merely by intensity and by being either of a negative or of a positive nature. Contrary to satisfaction, the anticlimax of the positive sensation of pleasure is the negative sensation of pain or discomfort. Neither of them possesses any direct quality. Only through the medium of other conjoint experiences do they acquire an indirect quality.

3. *Classification of Elementary Physical Phenomena*

We now classify all physical phenomena in quite the same manner as has already been done with psychological phenomena. We are unable to give any reason for the kind of classification chosen by us other than that the attempted classification will subsequently prove expedient. *Various forms of energy, forces, tensions, work performed, increase of entropy, acceleration and retardation of entropy increase,* are the six groups which contain all elementary physical phenomena we know of.

1.) By *various forms of energy* we understand mechanical, electrical, magnetic, thermal, chemical and other energies. Tension or energy may remain constant, as, for instance, in a floating body, in constant oscillations or in an explosive mixture, or it may be transformed by work, as occurs in the collision of mechanical bodies, in friction or in an explosion.

2.) *Forces* comprise mechanical, electrical, magnetic, thermal, chemical, frictional and surficial energy, to mention only a few. Forces may encounter an internal or an external resistance. In each of these, cases, tensions will result. An example of internal resistance is a swinging pendulum, i.e. a weight suspended on a cord, which is tautened. An example of external resistance is a weight resting on a stable base. In this case, the supporting base suffers a strain.

3.) *Tensions* are prevalent in the same physical domain, and need not be separately enumerated.

4.) *Work performed* is represented by any kind of transformation of energy. It occurs at any conversion of mechanical energy into heat and vice versa, as well as in any other transformation of energy. Work can be performed by a system or the system can be the object of work. In the first instance there is an active, in the second a passive change. A gas, for example, either "expands" or "is compressed," in other words, the gas is either active or it suffers the compression passively.

5.) We may use the concept of *entropy increase* as representing any process characterised by irreversibility or singleness of tendency, and thus for any process representing a transition into a more probable or stable state. Increase of entropy (dissipation of energy) is well marked in friction, combustion, explosions, chemical transformations, etc. Energy dissipation is approximately constant i.e. of steady intensity in metabolism and in periodically functioning machines as we have pointed out in detail in Part One.

6.) *Acceleration and the slowing down* (or retardation) *of entropy increase* represents a positive and a negative change of energy transformation, for instance, if normal metabolism is speeded up and slowed down, thus changing the approximately steady transformative intensity of energy dissipation. In Part One we have associated this kind of process with structural changes.

4. *Some Characteristics of the Six Groups of Physical Phenomena*

The *various forms of energy* are exceedingly numerous and endowed with a remarkable quality the nature of which is the main subject of the natural sciences. Some forms of energy may be mutually superjacent or subjacent without disturbing each other, others combine into new forms of energy, whilst still others cancel each other out and can under no circumstances co-exist in the same sections of space. We remind the reader of waves of a given amplitude, frequency and phase, which sometimes amplify or intensify, sometimes annul each other, but are always mutually superimposed. Energies have a variety of properties: we speak of kinetic or of potential energy, of powerful or of weak energy, and so on. Examples of measures of energy are $\frac{1}{2}$ mv^2 in mechanics and eV in electricity.

Forces are qualified by intensity and they may combine. Accordingly, two or more forces co-existing in the same place combine into one resulting force, the so-called *resultant*. Forces do not directly possess any quality; only with regard to their source or energy do we distinguish electrical from magnetic or other forces. Whether they are of electrical or magnetic origin is of no importance to their energy. An instance of this is the fact that *Millikan's* experiment with a drop of oil may be used for the determination of the elementary charge.

Tensions originate where forces are in opposition and meet with resistance. Like the pressure of gas, they may either be completely structureless and isotropic, or may also exhibit a tendency. Special forms of these are shearing stresses.

Entropy increase is one-dimensional, scalar and positive. It merely has quantity, but no quality, for according to thermodynamics a decrease of entropy is impossible if all processes within a closed system are considered. This does not, however, exclude a local decrease of entropy if supercompensated by a still larger increase somewhere else. A local decrease of entropy, i.e. the creation of free energy, is very well possible and constantly to be observed. In place of the term "entropy increase" we often prefer the term *relaxation of a tension* when discussing physiological or psychological problems.

Acceleration and the slowing down of entropy increase represents a temporal change of intensity of entropy increase, which is one-dimensional and without quality, distinguishable only by intensity and by positive and negative character. We often prefer the terms *acceleration, speeding up* and *slowing down, retardation, delay, inhibition of relaxation of a tension,* in case we are dealing with physiological or psychological problems.

The above groups are sharply separated from each other, without any gradual transition, just like the groups of psychological phenomena. In spite of this, there exist numerous connections and interrelations between the various groups. To throw light upon the interrelations of physical phenomena is the task of the natural sciences. We will deal only with some few that may be of importance to our purpose.

Every natural process is a phenomenon characterised not only by singleness of tendency, but also by relaxation. The latter is trivial if the concept of tension be defined as the feasibility of work performed, a local increase, viz. creation of free energy between latent and active tension, since frequently the latter only is defined as a tension at all.

If a system presents the possibility of relaxation of a physical tension, a force originates. Such a possibility is, therefore, the cause of a force. Gas compressed in an oxygen cylinder furnishes a good example in this respect. The expansion of the gas would involve relaxation or entropy. This possibility is the source of the pressure of the gas in the cylinder. An explosive mixture, however, lacks the possibility of relaxation or entropy as long as there is no ignition. Therefore, no forces develop in such a mixture.

Should two or more forces in opposition be mutually superimposed, internal and external resistance and drag would arise and result in tensions. This not only impedes relaxation but sometimes prevents it altogether. The inherent possibility of relaxation or entropy in any system is, as already stated, the source of a force, the relaxation itself representing the object of the force. If a force does not encounter a resistance of equal potency, it takes effect and results in work being performed and energy being converted.

The approach to an aim by the activation of a force is accompanied by relaxation. Every process represents the maximum possible degradation of energy. If a system is the object of work performed, a local increase, viz. creation of free energy may result. The mutual superimposition of several forces yields a resultant. The resultant differs from a single force essentially in that it does not meet with any resistance and takes effect in any case, because any existing resistance would already participate in the formation of the resultant. Thus the resultant is always followed by work performed, which is identical with a transformation of free energy into degraded energy which process is equivalent to relaxation.

The energetical condition of a system necessarily and unmistakably determines all other phenomena, i.e. all forces, potential resultants, tensions, work performed, increase of entropy or relaxation, acceleration and slowing down of relaxation or of entropy increase.

5. *Interrelations Linking the Separate Groups of Experiences and of Physical Phenomena*

The aforementioned groups of psychological and physical phenomena are markedly distinct from one another. They represent incommensurable magnitudes that are mutually as imcompatible as are ounce and inch or ounce and second. Despite this, there are many relations connecting the various groups. On the strength of the above classifications, the fundamental co-ordination of psychological and physical (physiological) phenomena becomes apparent of itself. We will exemplify only the few that seem to be important to our purpose.

The instincts and mental impulses result in a drive termed "will power," which is the joint product of them all. As soon as some of the instincts and impulses are in opposition, the will power is weakened by the less intense impulses and instincts. Impulses in opposition to volition form a mental resistance and give rise to inhibitions. An inner resistance manifests itself in reluctance, indecision, hesitation, aversion, disinclination, disgust, and loathing. Compare the two last sections of the previous chapter, and in the following the reader should always check with Chapters III and IV.

Unless willfulness encounters an insurmountable external obstacle, it is the source of an autonomous action. The aim of volition, as well as of instincts and impulses, is always the relaxation of a physical tension which is equivalent to entropy increase. Volition, like instincts and impulses, is, besides, directed toward all intermediate stages representing an approach to its aim.

Where there are no stresses and tensions, there are no impulses either, and contentment or satisfaction prevails. However, if existing physical tensions and stresses find no means of relaxation, we are discontented, dissatisfied, excited, irritated, annoyed, out of humor, and so on. The nearer we approach a desired relaxation, the stronger grows the feeling of pleasant anticipation. Instincts and impulses counteracting each other and a will power meeting with opposition will arouse mental tensions. Unappeased impulses are desires, hopes, longings, cravings, passions, expectations, and temptations.

A cognition evoking mental impulses, and thus influencing volition and actions, we may term a stimulus. Such stimuli are incitement, suggestion, stimulation, encouragement, buoyancy, verve, gusto, instigation, cheering, inspiration of hope, and so on. It is said, for instance, that the sight of food stimulates the appetite.

The relative increase or decrease of satisfaction is accompanied by the feeling of pleasure or pain respectively. External circumstances promoting aims and intentions and so provoking joy are called "good fortune" or "luck," whereas those frustrating our desires and aims and thus causing us pain are termed "misfortune" or "bad luck." Impediments to our volition or its liberation from external obstacles involve an increase or a diminution of satisfaction. Consequently the exertion of an influence upon will power may be experienced either as pleasure or as pain.

Satisfaction and emotion are accompanied by cognitions. We rejoice, feel gratified, or are displeased. The respective object of satisfaction indirectly furnishes the former with a quality. Here are some examples: satiety, creative vigor, the slaking of thirst, appeasement, terror of ghosts, famine, danger of war. Every recognized phenomenon capable of promoting the attainment of our aim or advantageous to the appeasement of an instinct or impulse excites our interest. If it is subservient to our purposes, we "like" or "love" it; if it represents an obstacle, we "dislike" or "hate" it. Our interest includes not only all "important" events, people, things, and other contents of cognitions, but also experiences. The "higher" the aim, the "purer" our love. Striving for beauty as such, we love everything beautiful.

Every mental action implies an exertion, a pulling together, a concentration, an effort, an expenditure of strength and energy, drudging, taking pains, slaving, and exhaustion. The power to overcome external obstacles by action is our "working capacity." The cognitions of this power or faculty are connected with a "feeling of vigor." This comprises strength, working capacity, endurance, ability, skill, self-assertion, fitness, self-confidence, self-reliance, judgment, and talent. Related to these are will power, strength of will, energy, resolution, elasticity, and initiative.

Any mental action is, moreover, accompanied by "fatigue." This comprises strain, weariness, lassitude, weakening, and exhaustion. The feeling of strength disappears with increasing fatigue, and we talk of weakness, feebleness, faintness, or tiredness. If the will power is absent, we speak of lack of energy, a weak will, indecision, or lethargy. Thus the cognitions unmistakably and inevitably contain all sensations, perceptions, and conceptions, i.e. all instincts and impulses, volition, actions, satisfaction, and emotions.

Positive feeling attitudes like joy, happiness, pleasure, will tend to increase the normal metabolic intensity of the organism and of organs, tissues, cells, while negative feeling attitudes like resentment, anxiety, discomfort, will tend to slow down the normal metabolic intensity. These correlations, however, are reversible. Artificial stimuli leading to an increase of metabolism will tend to produce positive feeling attitudes, while artificial inhibition of normal metabolism will tend to provoke negative feeling attitudes. And finally, inasmuch as we are in the position to consciously control our feelings, that is, the control of instinctive and emotional reactions, we actually can produce effects in our body similar to artificial stimuli.

The integration of all the psychological phenomena of an individual forms a unity or complex whole. This may be expressed by such terms as consciousness, soul, subject, ego, or I. The different groups of elementary psychological phenomena are co-ordinated to physical phenomena as suggested in the following table. This represents an attempt to co-ordinate psychological and physical terms by translating the one language into the other, and vice versa. One of the many implications of this little table of terms could be a first scientific approach to the still unsolved problems of how to measure desires, emotions, feeling of pain and pleasure, love, etc. The "Psychosomatic Dictionary" suggested by the author represents only the first step in the direction of placing psychoanalytic interpretation of emotional symptoms on a more scientific footing.

It might be objected that some of the psychophysical co-ordinations suggested by the above procedure are practically impossible. In spite of this, the author is convinced that any further attempt in this direction will at best improve our key. Moreover, the above contention is by no means novel, for at all times and with all peoples the idea has been a tradition more or less vaguely assumed. It is surely no mere coincidence that expressions like tension and relaxation, work and working power, energy and flexibility resistance and fatigue, full of energy and depressed, worn out, without energy, etc. are used in respect of inner experiences as well as of external phenomena. Words like "impulse" or "motive power" even seem already to constitute a synthesis of the two different domains. This clearly signifies more than a mere metaphor invented for the sake of illustration or for didactic purposes. We are probably not wrong in assuming that a dim presentiment of a co-ordination has sponsored the creation of these words belonging to both spheres alike.

Psychological Terms	Physical Terms
Actions in general	Transformation of energy, work performed
Activity of performance	Mechanical work performed
Cognitions	Various forms of energy, mostly electromagnetic and chemical
Conceptions, organic sensations	Energetical effects from within (the body), in brain, nervous system, etc.
Fatigue	Fatigue
Feeling of pleasure, joy, etc.	Accelerated relaxation of physical tension, accelerated energy transformation
Feeling of pain, discomfort, etc.	Retarded relaxation of physical tension, reduced energy transformation
Flexibility	Flexibility
Instincts, mental impulses	Forces, electrical impulses
Love, friendship, harmony	Mutually stabilizing functions based on cybernetics, harmonic bonds

Mental activity	Work performed by brain and nerves, electric rhythms
Passivity	Passivity
Perceptions	Compound of internal and external energies
Resistance, inhibitions	Resistance, drag
Satisfaction (of wants)	Relaxation of physical tension, steady transformative intensity (metabolism)
Sensations, sense-impressions	Energetic influence from without, from external objects
Tensions, stress	Tensions, stress
Violation, will power	Resultant of forces

Special attention should be given the interpretations of electroencephalograms in connection with the table of terms. In connection with that same table, it may be noted that medical men offer increasing evidence that the very development of certain pathological changes may result from physiological reactions to mental stress.

GLOSSARY OF MORE IMPORTANT TERMS

Amoeba: microscopic one-celled animal

Biocoenosis: an association of diverse organisms forming a natural unit, in which there is more or less obvious dependence or mutualism

Catalysis: acceleration of a reaction produced by a substance (catalyst) which may be recovered practically unchanged at the end of the reaction

Catenary: the shape assumed by a perfectly flexible cord in equilibrium under given forces

Chromosome: permanent structure in the cell nucleus, carrying the genes in linear arrangement

Cilia: hairlike processes found on many cells, capable of a vibratory movement

Cybernetics: comparative study of the control system formed by the nervous system and brain and mechano-electrical communication systems, such as computing machines

Cytology: the branch of biology treating of cells with reference to their structure, functions, multiplication, and life history

Cytoplasm: the protoplasm of the cell exclusive of the nucleus

Diagenesis: recombination or rearrangement resulting in a new product, as in the formation of larger crystalline grains from smaller ones

Electroencephalogram: reproduction of mostly rhythmical electrical impulses of the brain by very sensitive instruments

Entropy: a mathematical factor which is a measure of unavailable heat energy or of the degree of disorder

Entropy increase: a measure of degradation or dissipation of (heat) energy, relaxation of a tension

Entropy decrease or *negative entropy:* a measure of a local increase of available (heat) energy, of free energy

Flagellum: long, whiplike process of a cell. Flagella serve as swimming organs of many protozoa, bacteria, etc.

Free energy: available energy, negative entropy

Genes: material units of heredity capable of reproduction and mutation, linearly arranged in the chromosomes

Genotype: the total gene complement in an individual

Haptic: pertaining to the sense of touch

Homeostasis: the tendency of an organism to maintain within itself relatively stable conditions, as of temperature, chemical composition, or the like, by means of its own regulatory mechanism

Isochronal: uniform in time, recurring at regular intervals

Isomorphic: of identical or like form

Isothermal: occurring at a constant temperature

Isotropic: having the same properties in all directions

Kinaesthetic: referring to the sense whose organs lie in the muscles, tendons, and joints, and are stimulated by bodily tensions

Kinetic: pertaining to motion

Mandible: jawbone

Mitosis: cell division involving longitudinal splitting of the chromosomes and their equal distribution to the daughter cells

Monoplast: cell or cell element retaining its primary form

Mutation: sudden change in a gene which is permanently transmitted to the offspring

Nyctitropism: the tendency of certain plant organs to assume special "sleeping" positions at night

Ontology: the study of the ultimate nature of things

Orthogenesis: variation which in successive generations of an organism follows some particular line, evolving some new type irrespective of the effect of natural selection or other external factors

Phenotype: a type determined by the visible characters common to a group as distinguished from their hereditary characters

Photon: a quantum of radiant energy

Protozoon: animal whose chief characteristic is that the body consists of only a single cell, and that it reproduces by fission

Servomechanism: an apparatus that includes a power-driven mechanism, mostly an electric motor which supplements a primary control operated by a comparatively feeble force

Soma: all of any organism except the germ cells

Stratification: formation or arrangement in strata, or layers

Tectonic: pertaining to rock structures and external forms resulting from the deformation of the earth's crust

Thermodynamics: the science which treats of the mechanical actions or relations of heat

Thermokinematics: the study of the motion or motive power of heat

SELECTED BIBLIOGRAPHY

1. Alexander, S.: Space, Time and Deity (Cambridge 1927)
2. Arrhenius, S.: Das Werden der Welten (Leipzig 1908)
3. Bavink, B.: Ergebnisse und Probleme der Naturwissenschaften (Zürich 1948).
4. Becher, E.: Fremddienliche Zweckmässigkeit der Pflanzengallen (Leipzig 1917)
5. Berkeley, G.: Treatise concerning the Principles of Human Knowledge, Vol. I (Oxford 1871)
6. Bertalanffy, L.: Theoretische Biologie I/II (Berlin 1932-1942)
7. Bergson, H.: L'évolution créatrice (Paris 1907)
8. Bleuler, E.: Die Psychoide als Prinzip der organischen Entwicklung (Berlin 1935)
9. Blum, H. F.: Time's Arrow and Evolution (Princeton 1951)
10. Bridgman, P. W.: The Nature of Thermodynamics (Harvard Univ. Press 1943)
11. Bücher, C.: Arbeit und Rhythmus (Leipzig 1919)
12. Burke, J. B.: The Origin of Life. Its Physical Basis and Definition ((London 1906)
13. Bumke, O.: Gedanken über die Seele (Springer 1941)
14. Coker, R. E.: Some philosophical reflections of a biologist (Scient. Monthly 1939)
15. Cossmann, P. N.: Elemente der empirischen Teleologie (Stuttgart 1899)
16. Dewey, J.: Theory of Valuation, Internat. Encycl. of Unified Science, I, 1939
17. Dobzhansky, Th.: Die genetischen Grundlagen der Artbildung (Jena 1939)
18. Driesch, H.: Philosophie des Organischen (Leipzig 1928)
19. Eddington, A. S.: New Pathways of Science (Cambridge 1934)
20. Fechner, G. Th.: Einige Ideen zur Schöpfungs- und Entwicklungsgeschichte der Organismen (1877)
21. Feibleman, James K.: Ontology (Baltimore 1951)
22. Fireman, P.: Perceptualistic Theory of Knowledge (New York 1954)
23. Fischer, E.: Vitalismus und Pathologie (Berlin 1924)

24. Friedmann, H.: Die Welt der Formen (2 Bände, München 1930)
25. Frey-Wyssling, A.: Submicroscopic Morphology of Protoplasm and its Derivations. Protopl. Monogr. 15 (Berlin 1938)
26. Gamow, G.: The Birth and Death of the Sun (New York 1940)
27. Giedion, S.: Mechanisation takes Command (New York 1948)
28. Guye, Ch. E.: L'évolution physico-chimique (Paris 1942)
29. Haeckel, R.: Anthropologie oder Entwicklungsgeschichte des Menschen (Leipzig 1877)
30. Haldane, J. S.: The Philosophical Basis of Biology (London 1931)
31. Hartmann, M.: Allgemeine Biologie (Jena 1933)
32. Hartmann, N.: Der Aufbau der realen Welt (Berlin 1940)
33. Heberer, G.: Ergebnisse und Probleme der Abstammungslehre (Jena 1943)
34. Hertwig, O.: Das Werden der Organismen (Jena 1918)
35. Herbst, C.: Formative Reize in der tierischen Ontogenese (Leipzig 1901)
36. Herbart, J.: Lehrbuch der Psychologie (Königsberg 1834)
37. Hoyle, F.: The Nature of the Universe (Oxford 1950)
38. Hume, D.: An Enquiry Concerning Human Understanding, Essays and Treaties (London 1882)
39. Janisch, E.: Das Experimentalgesetz als Grundlage einer vergleichenden Biologie (Berlin 1927)
40. Jeans, J.: Physics and Philosophy (Cambridge University Press 1943)
41. Jensen, P.: Organische Zweckmässigkeit, Entwicklung und Vererbung vom Standpunkt des Physikers (Jena 1907)
42. Jordan. P.: Die Physik und das Geheimnis des organischen Lebens (Braunschweig 1943)
43. Jung, C. G.: Ueber die Energetik der Seele (Zürich 1928)
44. Korschelt, E.: Lebensdauer, Altern und Tod (Jena 1924)
45. Lavelle, L.: Introduction à l'ontologie (Paris 1947)
46. Leduc, St.: Théorie physico-chimique de la vie et génération spontanée (Paris 1910)
47. Lehmann, O.: Flüssige Kristalle und ihr scheinbares Leben (Leipzig 1921)
48. Lillie, R. S.: General Biology and Philosophy of Organism (Chicago 1945)
49. Miehe, H.: Das Archiplasma (Jena 1926)

50. Mc Dougall, W.: Psychology (Oxford 1945)
51. Molisch, H.: Populäre biologische Vorträge (Jean 1922)
52. Morgan, C. L.: A Concept of the Organism, emergent and resultant. Meet. Aristot. Soc. 1927
53. Nägeli, C. v.: Die Mizellartheorie, Ostwalds Klassiker d. Naturwissensch. 227, 1928
54. Neaf, A.: Die Vorstufen der Menschwerdung (Jena 1933)
55. Needham, J.: Order and Life (Cambridge 1936)
56. Noüy, Lecomte Du: Le Temps et la Vie (Paris 1936)
57. Oldenkop, E.: Ueber das hierarchische Prinzip in der Natur und seine Beziehungen zum Mechanismus-Vitalismus Problem (Reval 1930)
58. Ostwald, W.: Die Mühle des Lebens (Leipzig 1911)
59. Pauly, A.: Darwinismus u. Lamarckismus. Entwurf einer psychophysischen Teleologie (München 1905)
60. Peter, K.: Die Zweckmassigkeit in der Entwicklungsgeschichte (Berlin 1920)
61. Pearson, K.: The Grammar of Science (London 1900)
62. Pflüger, E.: Die teleologische Mechanik der lebendigen Natur, Arch. f. d. ges. Physiologie 15, 76, 1875 und Pflügers Arch. 15, 1877
63. Planck, M.: Thermodynamik (Berlin 1930)
64. Rashevsky, N.: Mathematical Biophysics (Chicago 1938)
65. Reinke, J.: Philosophie der Botanik (Leipzig 1905)
66. Rignano, E.: Das Gedächtnis als Grundlage des Lebendigen (Leipzig 1931)
67. Russell B.: The Analysis of Mind, 1921
68. Russell, E. S.: The Directiveness of Organic Activities (Cambridge 1945)
69. Scientific American Reader (Simon and Schuster, New York 1953)
70. Schrödinger, E.: What is Life? (Cambridge University Press 1944)
71. Semon, A.: Die Mneme (Leipzig 1920)
72. Schultz, J.: Leib und Seele (Berlin 1923)
73. Sherrington, C. S.: Man on his Nature (Cambridge 1940)
74. Spann, O.: Naturphilosophie (Jena 1937)
75. Speemann, H.: Experimentelle Beiträge zu einer Theorie der Entwicklung (Berlin 1936)
76. Staudinger H.: Makromolekulare Chemie und Biologie (Basel 1947)
77. Taylor, A. E.: Does God Exist? (1945)

78. Timoféeff-Ressovsky, N. W.: Experimentelle Mutations-forschung in der Vererbungslehre (Leipzig 1937)
79. Thyssen-Bornemisza, S.: Das Wesen des Lebens und der Seele (Zürich 1949)
80. Trotter, W.: Science and Philosophy (Nature 1930)
81. Uexküll, J. v.: Theoretische Biologie (Berlin 1928)
82. Vogt, W.: Road to Survival (New York 1948)
83. Walter, W. Grey.: The Living Brain (New York 1953)
84. Whitehead, A. N.: The Concept of Nature (Cambridge 1926)
85. Wolff, G.: Leben und Erkennen (München 1933)
86. Woltereck, R.: Grundzüge einer allgemeinen Biologie (Stuttgart 1940)
87. Woodger, J. H.: Biological Principles (London 1929)
88. Wundt, W.: Grundzüge der physiologischen Philosophie (Leipzig 1902)
89. Ziehen, Th.: Die Beziehungen der Lebenserscheinungen zum Bewusstsein (Berlin 1921)
90. Zwicky, F.: On Supernovae, Bull. Astr. Soc. Pacific 50 (1938)